LAKE RAMSAY, BELL PARK

# SUDBURY BASIN

## BASIN

*The Story of Nickel*

D. M. LeBOURDAIS

THE RYERSON PRESS — TORONTO

*Published December, 1953*

PRINTED AND BOUND IN CANADA
BY THE RYERSON PRESS, TORONTO

*To*

## MY WIFE

WHO FOR UPWARDS
OF TWO YEARS HAS
SHARED ME WITH

### SUDBURY

# PREFACE

IN JULY, 1951, H. J. FRASER, VICE-PRESIDENT
and general manager of Falconbridge Nickel
Mines Limited, in talking about books that should be
written, asked me if I had ever considered doing a book on
Sudbury. He said that as the centre of the world's nickel
industry, if for no other reason, it should be an interesting
subject and he felt that Sudbury's story should be told
before it slipped from the memories of such pioneers as
might still be living. He said he had once thought he might
do it himself, but now knew he would never get the time.

I replied that although I had frequently been in Sudbury
and realized its interest and importance, I had never
thought of it as the subject of a book. In the next few
months, however, it seemed that scarcely a day passed that
I did not read or hear some reference to Sudbury. Consequently, when I was planning at the end of the year what
I should be doing in 1953 I thought of Sudbury and wrote
Mr. Fraser a note asking if he was still interested in the
subject. He was; and as a result I have devoted a large part
of the past two years to writing this book, the cost of which
has been underwritten by Falconbridge Nickel Mines
Limited.

Although I have spent much of the interval in Sudbury,
and have read everything I could find on the subject,
I could not have written the book without the help of
many persons, whom I wish to thank. In the first place,
I should like to express my sincere appreciation of the
co-operation I have had at all times from Falconbridge
Nickel Mines Limited and its officers, especially Messrs.
Fraser, Mott and Lockhead.

I should also like to acknowledge my obligation to the late R. Leslie Beattie and his successor, J. Roy Gordon, vice-president in charge of Canadian operations of the International Nickel Company of Canada, Limited, for the opportunity to see something of that company's operations, and to D. M. Dunbar for piloting me round.

My frequent visits to Sudbury were made comfortable and in every way agreeable by the unfailing courtesy and consideration of Al. Rouleau, proprietor of the Nickel Range Hotel, and his staff, to whom my thanks are due.

To Messrs. W. E. W. and S. A. H. Cressey I am indebted for permission to examine the files of the Sudbury *Journal*, without which I should have had much more difficulty in gathering material concerning the early days of Sudbury.

Among those who were particularly helpful in providing material and in checking over various parts of my manuscript, I should like to thank Charles Dorian, writer on the early history of Sudbury, Mrs. J. S. Legris who, born Beatrice Frawley, has lived in Sudbury all her life and has also written about it, and Mrs. Olivier Leduc, daughter of Stephen Fournier. I should like also to thank Rev. Father Lorenzo Cadieux, S.J., founder and director of the Northern Ontario Historical Society, and Miss Isabel McLean, Librarian of the Public Library, for historical material supplied. For giving me the benefit of what they remember, I am grateful to H. P. MeKeown, for twenty years until his retirement in 1951, city clerk of Sudbury; and to A. J. Manley, resident of Sudbury since 1905 and Sheriff since 1932.

N. F. Parkinson, of Toronto, former secretary of Falconbridge Nickel Mines Limited, now Executive Director of the Ontario Mining Association, has helped with both information and advice.

I should also like to acknowledge my indebtedness to Richard P. Baine for granting me access to his thesis, *The Settlement of Sudbury Region*, completed by him in 1952 for his M.A. degree in the University of Toronto, which

has helped me to understand better some aspects of the
Sudbury region, and for permission to reproduce the map
on page 189.

Mrs. A. P. Turner very kindly supplied me with copies
of unpublished manuscripts by her husband and by
D. H. Browne, from which I have quoted.

The photographs opposite pages 34, 114, 115 and that
of William E. Mason were supplied by the Sudbury daily
*Star*.

Responsibility for everything that appears in the book is
wholly mine, and I regret that it has been impossible for me
to include reference to many who have played a part in
Sudbury's history and that when people or events are
mentioned the reference may seem inadequate.

D. M. LEB.

TORONTO, *November 10, 1953.*

# CONTENTS

# LIST OF ILLUSTRATIONS

## MAPS

# I

# *Preview*

THE METAL AGE IS BRINGING A NEW TYPE of civilization to Canada. One Canadian community can point to an existence of more than half a century during which it has depended entirely upon the production of metal. This by itself would, of course, mean nothing. But it is undoubtedly the forerunner of many others which in the years to come will dot Canada's northern hinterland. It may be typical of the future Canada in another way. In its veins courses the blood of people drawn from the four corners of the earth to produce a commodity serving the whole world. Ninety per cent of the world's nickel is mined at Sudbury, Ontario.

While far south of the geographical centre of the province, in latitude 46° 30′ N. (long. 81° W.), Sudbury is considered to be in *northern* Ontario, because geologically, climatically and in every other way it belongs to that vast region comprising the greater part of Ontario and nearly two-thirds of Canada called the Canadian Shield, in people's minds generally associated with the North. Nevertheless it is within forty miles of Lake Huron.

The Shield is now known to be one of the world's greatest mineral storehouses, which, with the wealth of the Cordilleran belt of British Columbia and the Yukon, establishes Canada as pre-eminently a metal-producing country. No longer is the grain elevator Canada's most characteristic structure, for the mine headframe is about to supplant it.

1

The Shield and the Cordilleran region of the West also constitute one of the world's greatest timber areas which, with proper conservation, can provide a continuing supply of wood products. These, under the wizardry of modern chemistry, can be transformed into an infinite variety of synthetics of all sorts.

Streams, rushing down cataracts or tumbling over falls, provide an inexhaustible source of hydro-electric energy. And, as if this were not enough, the Shield is also the source of uranium, raw material of atomic power.

On the prairies, which once seemed destined to remain purely agricultural, extensive oilfields are being developed, providing additional power and raw materials for all of Canada. Petroleum and natural gas could alone supply a sound basis for a nation's economy.

It is axiomatic that a people's culture invariably derives from its ways of making a living. Hitherto all civilizations have had an agricultural basis; but, even now, Canada is evolving a totally different type of civilization, one based on metals, synthetics and power.

Sudbury offers a testing-ground for this new orientation. Its history of more than half a century already suggests the way of the future. It provides new opportunities for people, both immigrants and native-born; and it is possible that in its schools and playgrounds the visage of the most typical Canadian may some day be seen. That Canadian will be derived from the two dozen nationalities which make up Sudbury's population.

Towns and cities attain importance in the world because of some natural advantage, such as a harbour, the confluence of rivers, or nearby arable lands. But Sudbury's origin is due to nothing of the kind; choice of its site was purely accidental.

As construction of the Canadian Pacific in the early eighties continued across the Canadian Shield of Ontario from the Ottawa River to Lake Superior, successive centres of activity were set up, and, as the steel pushed farther west, each in turn became a collection of largely-abandoned shacks. Mattawa, North Bay, Sturgeon Falls, each had been one of these; now it was Sudbury's turn.

Although not as bare and gaunt as it was later rendered by forest fires and sulphur fumes, Sudbury's site had little to commend it. Set as it was among a confusion of rocky hills, evidently those who selected it little dreamt that it might one day become a thriving city. It was merely one of a thousand others beside the tracks of Canada's first transcontinental.

A few miles to the northwest, the right-of-way passed out of the hills onto the surface of what seemed to be a valley nearly twenty miles across; but when it had reached the other side it continued on through typical Shield country.

On every side the land was covered by timber, most of which had been too far from logging-streams; but now the railway provided a market, as well as trade for the few small stores that had been established among the cluster of shacks. For some years the timber trade was to mean much to Sudbury, and its first well-to-do citizens were connected with lumbering. But as the stands receded with cutting this business gradually grew less.

It might have seemed that Sudbury had reached the end of its possibilities. But the railway had helped to bring to light a product that was to launch Sudbury upon a unique career. Three miles beyond, the grading-crews cut through a ledge of mineral-bearing rock. Speculators bought the land from the provincial government and it later became a mine.

Word of this mineral occurrence quickly reached prospectors over the never-failing "grapevine," and soon they were combing the nearby hills. They then discovered that the valley lying to the west was really an oval basin, about thirty-eight miles long and about seventeen miles at its widest, and that the most likely places for mineral were in the hills forming the basin's edge.

These mineralized spots were not hard to find, for they were usually marked by heavily stained "burns" or "gossan," often bare of vegetation. Within a short while

the prospectors had located most of the outcrops, and some
of the most famous mines in the Sudbury district now bear
their names.

The ore was complex, in some places containing high
copper values; but eventually it was learned that in other
places the ore contained even greater values of nickel.   This
graphically changed the picture, for nickel posed difficult
metallurgical problems, and as yet a market for that metal
scarcely existed.

While the prospectors and miners were busy with these
affairs, others not so directly concerned with mining were
grappling with the problem of building a community,
although few, if any, really thought of it in that way.   For
one reason or another they had remained behind when the
construction gangs moved on, hoping that this might prove
to be the place they were looking for.

During construction the C.P.R. had operated a boarding
house.   It was now taken over and run by its former
manager on his own behalf.   Men with business experience
ordered goods from Montreal wholesale houses and, pending
more permanent buildings, opened stores in tents or shacks
abandoned by the railway workers.

Doctors arrived with the construction crews, and one or
two threw in their lot with the new community; soon there
were lawyers as well.   During construction no liquor was
sold (legally), but as the end of steel moved on saloons
were opened and a few prostitutes began to ply their trade.
Hot on the heels of vice came the clergy.

The first street was the tote road which had preceded
the railway grade, and the new settlement straggled along
its sides.   Two streams converged nearby, their channels
providing the only breaks, aside from the raw slashings of
the tote road and right-of-way, through the dense bush.

Sudbury in these days was a typical frontier community.
Although on the main line of the C.P.R., it was isolated,
its only neighbours being similar railway stops.   The
nearest large city, Montreal, was 438 miles to the east,

while Toronto, by way of North Bay, was 308 miles distant. The telephone did not arrive for many years, and telegrams, being expensive, were used only in cases of emergency.

The first work train reached Sudbury in November, 1883. The population attained a peak of about 1,500, mostly males; but with the shift of activity further west, this dropped to about 300, to form the nucleus of the village of Sudbury.

As mines were developed, small communities grew about them, chief of which was Copper Cliff, where the first mines were opened and the first smelting begun. In the early uncertain days of the nickel industry, these communities (as well as Sudbury itself) had an uneasy existence, flourishing while the mines were active and languishing when they were closed down.

In 1887 the C.P.R., which owned the townsite, had it surveyed. For many years the streets were no more substantial than lines on a map; but Sudbury continued to grow and by 1893, with a population of 1,000, had been incorporated as a town. It was yet without sidewalks, and sewage ran in the gutters. Most of the citizens got their drinking water from a spring that bubbled out of a gravel pit, and householders paid a water-peddler to keep their barrels filled.

Meanwhile, in 1888, the first smelter had been blown in at Copper Cliff, and another in 1890 at the Murray Mine, where the railway grade had first disclosed mineral. In the same year that Sudbury became a town, Col. Robert M. Thompson, in New Jersey, and Carl Langer, an employee of the Mond chemical works in England, succeeded independently in developing processes for the separation of nickel from nickel-copper ores.

Sudbury took a step forward in 1897, when a system of electric light, waterworks and sewage disposal was installed. No longer were citizens dependent upon the vagaries of the water-vendor. Another step was taken in 1902, when the Bell Telephone Company wired Sudbury and Copper Cliff for their first telephones.

Of immense importance to the district was the incorporation in 1900 of the Mond Nickel Company. In 1901 production started at the famous Creighton mine. In the same year Thomas A. Edison visited the town, and subsequently acquired mining property in Falconbridge township. But perhaps the most important event of that period was the merging, in 1902, of the Orford Copper Company and the Canadian Copper Company to constitute the International Nickel Company.

In 1913 the Department of Mines, Ottawa, published a comprehensive report on the nickel industry by Dr. A. P. Coleman, the result of studies of the geology of the Sudbury nickel irruptive continuing over many years.

With the outbreak of World War I, nickel, which had been steadily growing in economic importance, became of prime significance. Fear that the metal might be reaching the Germans led the Ontario government to appoint a Royal Commission to study and report upon the nickel industry, not only in Canada but elsewhere; and its report, published in 1917, marked a milestone in the history of that industry.

The International Nickel Company of Canada was incorporated in 1916, and in the same year that company began construction of a nickel refinery at Port Colborne, Ontario. Also in 1916, nickel deposits in Falconbridge township, indicated in 1901 by Edison's dip-needle surveys, were definitely located by the drills of the E. J. Longyear Company.

In the meantime, Sudbury had been emerging from its isolation. In 1900, the C.P.R. had completed its line from Sudbury to Sault Ste. Marie, thus providing connections with Chicago and the western United States. In 1908 the C.P.R. opened its branch from Romford, on the mainline three miles east of Sudbury, to Toronto; and in the same year the Canadian Northern (now the Canadian National) completed a line from Toronto to Capreol, connecting with Sudbury by a branch from Sudbury Junction. In 1912, Sudbury was linked with North Bay by highway.

Although a weekly newspaper had begun publication in 1891 and several others had been published intermittently, it was not till 1909 that a daily newspaper was launched. The latter was to provide an opportunity for one of Sudbury's most interesting citizens.

The end of World War I found the production of nickel greatly increased over pre-war levels, while the demand had suddenly slackened. Mines closed down and there was much hardship. To counteract this, Inco and Mond devoted a great deal of attention to promoting additional uses for nickel. This was made easier by the growth of the automotive industry, with its need for materials combining lightness, strength, and the ability to withstand high temperatures.

Then, in 1929, the International Nickel Company of Canada and the Mond Nickel Company were united. For some time they had been finding their objectives running along similar lines; but what finally led to the merger was the fact that they were owners at opposite ends of a great nickel deposit which could be more economically developed by a single operation.

A year before Inco and Mond joined forces a company was incorporated which in the years to come was to play an increasing part in the nickel industry. In 1928 Falconbridge Nickel Mines Limited was formed to develop the properties formerly owned by Thomas A. Edison, held in the interval by the E. J. Longyear Co. and others. In 1930, Falconbridge's first smelter unit was blown in.

The year 1930 was notable also for the beginning of electrolytic copper refining at Copper Cliff by the Ontario Refining Company, a subsidiary of Inco, while nitre cake and sulphuric acid were first produced from smelter by-products at Copper Cliff by Canadian Industries Limited.

During the boom conditions of the late twenties, the population of Sudbury had jumped to 20,000 and in 1930 the town was incorporated as a city. By now it had become established as the commercial, judicial and political centre of an extensive district.

With the depression hard times came to Sudbury, in common with the rest of the country. But Sudbury was especially vulnerable, since it was dependent upon a single industry, and the demand for the product of that industry had decreased enormously. The city was forced to default on its debentures, and for some years its financial affairs were administered by a receiver.

Improvement in conditions was largely due to the initiative of the nickel companies in finding new uses and enlarged markets for their products. With the renewed threat of war, the call for nickel again became incessant and this was reflected in the fortunes of the community. When war actually broke out, demands were made upon the mining companies such as had never before been made. The achievement of Inco in increasing its capacity by the installation of new plant and equipment, without even a temporary loss in production, was an engineering feat of the first magnitude.

The end of World War II found Sudbury a vigorous city of about 40,000 people, with another 15,000 in the surrounding communities, and the centre of an industry that affected the whole world. Its people, appropriately enough, were drawn from nearly every country. While some of these tended to live in groups and preserve the racial characteristics of other lands, Sudbury had begun to evolve a type of citizen which might well become distinctively Canadian.

During all this time, the smelters had been fed from mines located by prospectors in the eighties and nineties. But in the post-war years, the initiative of Falconbridge Nickel Mines Limited brought about the discovery of important new ore-bodies, chiefly along the north rim.

Within the basin, Ontario Pyrites Limited, a Ventures subsidiary, had re-opened copper-lead-zinc-silver mines that had been worked for a time in the twenties, with a good prospect of providing Sudbury with additional raw materials for the industries of the future.

Sudbury's next step was already obvious, although not much was yet done about it. With a wide variety of raw materials, and with an efficient labour supply, only cheaper power and better transportation were required to establish Sudbury as an important manufacturing centre. Both the power and the improved transportation seemed possibilities of the near future. Natural gas from the West might provide one and completion of the St. Lawrence Waterway the other.

Thus Sudbury epitomizes the evolution of a Canadian frontier community into an important city, which has occurred within the life span of many now living in the district. It is to be hoped that the following record will not only prove of current interest but may also have continuing value in interpreting the heritage of this community when it has further fulfilled its obvious destiny.

# II

# *Earth's Travail*

EXCEPT FOR AN OCCASIONAL EARTHQUAKE and here and there a volcano, the earth seems the most stable thing we know. We think of it when we wish to suggest something solid and unyielding. Yet it was not always so. There have been times when, in many parts of the globe, the earth's crust has twisted and buckled, and mountain ranges have appeared where once there were none.

During a period extending from a thousand million to fifteen hundred million years, the northeastern two-thirds of what is now Canada was repeatedly subjected to immense pressures and high mountains were pushed up in the form of a huge U around the depression we now call Hudson Bay.

In this mountain-building process, masses of molten material, forced from far below, welled upward along a line of weakness into or near the surface rocks, often bringing minerals, also in a molten state, which, as the mass cooled, were precipitated, generally at the point of contact between the intrusive (new material) and the surrounding rocks.

Meanwhile, rain, frost and other wearing-down agencies were busy restoring to a common level the mountains thus thrust up. (Geologists estimate that about thirty million years are required to wear down a mountain to a fairly level plateau). Seas and other depressions were filled with silt carried by streams from the high land. Sometimes the weight of this newer land caused it to sink into the earth's crust, thus causing land elsewhere to rise.   In some cases the readjustment took the form of faults or shears, often providing opportunities for the deposition of minerals in these fissures or crevices.

Then, much later in the geologic scale, a time came when the winters were longer and the summers shorter until the snow that fell in winter could no longer thaw during the summer.   Snow under pressure of its own weight soon turns to ice and in a short while large portions of the northern hemisphere, including nearly all of Canada and part of the United States, were covered by an ice-sheet, in places several thousand feet thick.

Like the crust of the earth itself, ice is not rigid, but is forever on the move.   Ice that formed near Hudson Bay, under pressure from thicker icefields farther north, moved southward until melted in a warmer climate.   Owing to its weight, this ice in the course of its movement across the continent literally planed and scraped the face of the land, grinding the underlying rocks to powder.

As the icecap melted, lakes—some immense—were formed on its southern edge, and in these the rock powder was deposited to form much of the fertile farmlands of the Great Plains region of Canada and the United States.   But the greater part of northeastern Canada, now constituting what we call the Canadian Shield, was stripped bare, or almost bare, leaving exposed the granites and other igneous rocks which once lay deep within the earth's crust.   In some places the surface is covered with clay, gravel or sand, often strewn helter-skelter.

Rock, water and trees are the Shield's chief characteristics.   Sometimes water seems to predominate, the land itself seemingly but a series of islands in a vast lake.   But elsewhere rock is more in evidence.   Toward the far north, beyond the tree-line, the land is covered with grasses and mosses which once provided forage for great herds of grazing animals.

One of the most striking features of the Shield is its level character.   People think of the prairie as a flat plain, stretching to the horizon on all sides without any apparent change in altitude.   But a far greater variation exists in the prairie-level than in the Canadian Shield.

For example, the prairie at Winnipeg is about 770 feet above the sea; in central Saskatchewan it is about 2,500 feet; and in western Alberta, about 3,500 feet.   Yet the Shield, which covers a much greater area, rises in only a few places to more than 2,000 feet above the sea, and rarely drops below the 1,000-foot level.   But between the 1,000- and 2,000-foot levels there is an endless variation.

The Shield is covered with an infinite variety of mounds, knobs, ridges and hills, seemingly jumbled about without any sort of system, although upon closer observation it can be seen that most of these, in any area, lie in the same general direction.   Another characteristic is that the tops of these hills or knobs are pretty much on a level.   In other words, the *surface* of the Shield really consists of the higher points, while the gullies, valleys and swales have been gouged out and lie below the general level.

In these lower spots water has collected to form myriads of lakes, from mere ponds to inland seas.   Nearly all lie in rocky basins of irregular outline, strung like beads on a string along the courses of twisting streams which drop over cliffs or plunge down rapids until they empty into a river destined for the sea.

The Canadian Shield comprises part of the island of Newfoundland, all of Labrador, the greater part of Quebec and Ontario, more than half of Manitoba, more than one-third of Saskatchewan, a small corner of Alberta, practically all of the district of Mackenzie, all of the district of Kee-watin, and portions of the Canadian Arctic Archipelago.

Its southern boundary follows the north shore of the Gulf of St. Lawrence and the river, nearly to Montreal, then swinging westward along the north shore of the Ottawa River to about the city of Ottawa, turns southward to touch the St. Lawrence again at the Thousand Islands.   From that point it cuts across the top of Old Ontario to the south-eastern angle of Georgian Bay.   Resting on the north shore of Lakes Huron and Superior, it crosses into the United States between Superior and Lake of the Woods. From Lake of the Woods the Shield's southwestern edge runs northwestward through Lakes Winnipeg, Athabaska, Great Slave and Great Bear to the Arctic Ocean.

In addition to being Canada's outstanding physiographic feature, the Shield is probably its most important economic factor, one which, more than any other, will in time set its mark upon the rest of Canada. Until comparatively recently, it was considered a liability, a limiting factor under whose influence Canada must always remain a relatively small and unimportant country. As late as 1947, a Canadian historian could write that the Shield was an "immense and forbidding mass." He was a historian, not a prophet, and merely recorded the prevailing view, not perhaps among explorers, geologists, mining engineers, or the growing number living in the Shield, but among Canadians generally.

Evidence produced within recent years by prospectors, mining companies and both federal and provincial Geological Surveys supports the belief that the Canadian Shield is one of the world's most highly mineralized regions. Already, with only a small portion of its vast extent even superficially prospected, extensive deposits of most of the metals essential to industry, in addition to rare and precious metals, have been found.

Immense deposits of iron ore are now being developed in Labrador, northern Quebec and northwestern Ontario. Copper is being produced in that section of Quebec extending from Noranda to Val d'Or, at Sudbury, and at Flin Flon; and new deposits are being developed in Gaspé and Chibougamau, as well as in various places in the Northwest Territories. Lead is being produced in the Noranda-Val d'Or region, and new deposits are being developed on the south shore of Great Slave Lake, while extensive resources exist on the east shore of Hudson Bay. Zinc is usually found with lead, and also in association with other minerals, as at Flin Flon. Gold is found in nearly every section of the Shield. Nickel and copper usually go together, and this combination is found in the Sudbury Basin and at a number of places in northern Manitoba.

Mining in the Shield goes back to the days before Confederation. More than thirty years before that historic event, in what was then Canada West, copper deposits rich enough to justify shipping ore to England were worked near the western end of the north shore of Georgian Bay. In 1846, the Montreal Mining Company began operations at Bruce Mines. Two years later, Sir William Logan, director of the Geological Survey of Canada, visited the region and reported ore running to 8.01 per cent copper.

Unfortunately, after a few years the veins began to pinch out, and their mineral content diminished with depth. The deepest shaft was 306 feet. The final estimate as to production for the region during the active period which ended in 1875, was 9,653 tons of copper, valued at $3,300,000. Subsequent attempts to open some of the mines were unsuccessful, and eventually the once-thriving community became one of the ghost-towns so often associated with mining.

Nickel was first discovered in Ontario at the Wallace mine, a short distance west of the point where the Whitefish River flows into Lake Huron. Alexander Murray, a staff-member of the Geological Survey of Canada, continuing in 1848 a survey of the north shore of Lake Huron, visited the mine in the course of his work. He reported a shallow shaft had been put down by the Upper Canada Mining Company and a channel in the surface rock cut for a short distance on both sides. No mining was in progress at the time, and the workings were filled with water, rendering a proper examination impossible. He secured samples of mineralized rock which on analysis showed: iron, 41.79 per cent; nickel-cobalt, 13.93; arsenic, 6.02; sulphur, 38.16; copper, 0.10. The prospect, however, was not further developed, and subsequent investigation failed to disclose any vein or mineralized mass which might suggest the possibility of a mine.

Even when the future nickel range was stumbled upon it was not recognized. In 1856 A. P. Salter, P.L.S., was engaged in running base, meridian and range lines in preparation for a general survey of the territory between Lake Nipissing and Sault Ste. Marie. From a point on Sturgeon River, near its mouth, he ran a base line westward to Whitefish Lake, and from there surveyed a meridian line twelve miles due north (continuing eighteen miles farther the following year).

In his report Salter mentioned that "between the fifth and eighth mile on this line I discovered considerable local attraction, the needle varying from four degrees to fourteen degrees westerly. The existence of iron was plainly discernible on the rock." Meeting Murray, who was continuing his geological explorations, he described the vagaries of the needle, giving Murray particulars of the exact locality.

Murray, in reporting on his season's work, tells of how he followed up Salter's hint:

At the fifth mile a dingy green magnetic trap, with a large amount of iron pyrites, forms a ridge, and that rock, with syenite, continues in a succession of parallel ridges to the seventh mile, beyond which the country becomes low and marshy. These parallel ridges strike nearly east and west, and small brooks or marshes occupy the intermediate valleys.

Previous to my visit to Whitefish Lake, I had been informed by Mr. Salter that local attraction of the magnet had been observed by himself, while he was engaged in running the meridian line, and he expressed it to be his opinion that the presence of a large body of iron ore was the immediate cause. When, therefore, I came to the part indicated by Mr. Salter, I made a very careful examination not only in the direction of the meridian line, but for a considerable distance on each side of it, and the result of my examination was that the local attraction, which I found exactly as described by Mr. Salter, was owing to an immense mass of magnetic trap.

The compass was found, while traversing these trap ridges, to be deflected from its true bearing upwards of ten degrees at several different parts, and in one place it showed a variation of fifteen degrees west of the true meridian, or about twelve degrees from the true magnetic north. Specimens of this trap have been

given to Mr. Hunt [Sterry Hunt, assayer for the Geological
Survey] for analysis, and the result of his investigation shows that
it contains magnetic iron ore and magnetic iron pyrites generally
disseminated through the rock, the former in very small grains;
titaniferous iron was found associated with magnetic ore, and a
small quantity of nickel and copper with pyrites.

Today, such an account appearing in a Geological
Survey report would receive the immediate attention of
prospectors and mining companies, and the deposit would
be thoroughly examined.   In 1856, such a slight copper
showing at a spot in the wilderness forty miles from the
lake, with no means of transportation, was not such as
to attract prospectors, while the indication of nickel was
even less attractive.

Unknown to himself, Murray was on historic ground.
He and Salter were the first to walk over the spot which one
day would become the site of the greatest nickel mine in
the world.   In 1883, Salter's meridian became the west
boundary of Waters and Snyder townships, surveyed in
that year apparently without exciting any further mining
interest.   But when in the same year railway construction
opened up the country to prospectors the nickel industry
had its beginnings, and the years to come were to prove
that the Sudbury Basin was unique not only in so far as the
Canadian Shield was concerned, but as regards the whole
world.

The basin is a "lopolith" shaped like a square-sterned
skiff, about thirty-eight miles long by about seventeen
miles at its greatest width, striking approximately northeast
and southwest.   Except for its southeast corner, the portion
at the edge dips inward at between thirty and seventy
degrees. Geologists estimate that probably during Keweena-
wan time a mass of molten matter deep within the earth was
forced by subterranean pressure toward the surface.
Checked in its course by solid layers of sediments (Animiki),
this molten stream spread out between the base of the
sediments and the rocks below, causing considerable
deformation in the sediments.

Up to this point the geologists are fairly unanimous, but one group believe that after the intrusive had been squeezed into position, and during the cooling, it separated into layers.   The lighter, more acid, portions moved upward to crystallize into "micropegmatite," a granitic rock, while the heavier, more basic, portions sank to the bottom to form "norite."   A transition zone partaking somewhat of both separates the two.

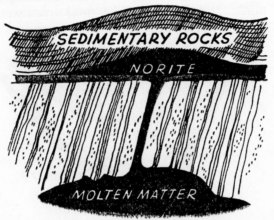

*Molten matter, forced up through the earth's crust, came in contact with the under side of layers of overlying sedimentary rocks and spread out.*

Then, owing to the weight of overlying sediments and lack of underlying support, the centre of the intrusive mass sank into the chasm from which it had emerged, displacing and disrupting the formations newly established as well as the sediments above, which ultimately settled into their present synclinal position.

The other view is that two more or less distinct upward thrusts occurred.   The first comprised the norite intrusion which was injected directly into its basin shape.   This was followed by a second upward thrust of the micropegmatite along the upper side of the norite.

NOTE: The illustrations on this and the following page are reproduced from *The Romance of Nickel*, Published by The International Nickel Company of Canada, Limited.

So much for the rocks that form the Basin. The nickel-copper ores that make the Basin famous are found in cracks and crevices along the under-side of the norite, and in places penetrating the older rocks lying below. Sometimes the ore is found as pockets in narrow bands of norite that extend some two or more miles away from the Basin.

Here again there are two questions. Did the ores travel with the norite and settle out like mud from water or did they follow behind the norite along the same trails?

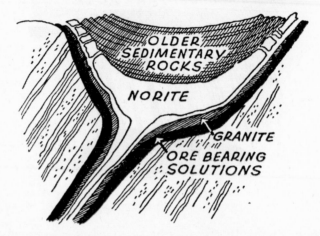

*Cross section of Sudbury Basin as geologists believe it exists today.*

The principal ore minerals are pyrrhotite (iron sulphide), pentlandite (nickel-iron sulphide) and chalcopyrite (copper-iron sulphide), the two latter being diffused throughout the former. The ore minerals, together with quartz, other gangue minerals and fragments of the enclosing rock form orebodies ranging from a few thousand to many millions of tons. For example, the orebody at Falconbridge is a more or less continuous tabular sheet of ore some 6,000 feet long, extending in depth for an unknown distance beyond 5,500 feet, with an average thickness of fifteen feet or more and containing several tens of millions of tons of ore.

Except for the eastern section, where the overburden is from 50 to 250 feet thick, frequent ore exposures occur along the contact between the norite and older formations. And it was the weathering of these exposures producing the highly coloured oxides of copper and iron that first attracted the attention of prospectors and led to the early discovery of the principal mineral deposits.

## TABLE OF FORMATIONS

| Geological Era | Geological Period | Type of Formation | Time Scale in Years |
|---|---|---|---|
| Cenozoic | Pleistocene | Sands, gravels and lacustrine silts | 0 to 1,000,000 |
| | LONG PERIOD OF EROSION | | |
| | | | 1,000,000 to 500,000,000 |
| Pre-Cambrian | Keweenawan | Basic dikes and sills (including Sudbury nickel irruptive and granite intrusions) | 500,000,000 |
| | | Sediments (Whitewater) | |
| | PERIOD OF EROSION | | |
| | Huronian | Basic dikes and sills and granite intrusions | |
| | PERIOD OF INTENSE FOLDING | | to |
| | Huronian | Sediments | |
| | LONG PERIOD OF FOLDING AND EROSION | | |
| | Algoman | Granite intrusion and granitization | |
| | Temiskaming | Sediments | |
| | Keewatin | Lavas | 200,000,000 |

# III

# *Westward the Steel*

WHEN IN 1869 THE NEWLY FORMED
Dominion of Canada took over the vast
north-western territory formerly controlled by the Hudson's
Bay Company, the eventual building of a railway to connect
that region with the east became inevitable; and in 1871,
when British Columbia joined Confederation, the building
of such a railway was one of the conditions of union.

Despite this, much doubt existed as to whether so
ambitious an undertaking could ever be financed by the
young Dominion, and whether such a railway could be made
to pay. For a time it was proposed to build only west of
the Great Lakes, where the line could be operated when the
lakes were free of ice. In 1880, however, a contract was
entered into between the Government of Canada and a
syndicate of financiers who undertook, in consideration of
certain subsidies and other assistance, to build the line
and operate it.

The Canadian Pacific Railway Company was incorporated to carry out the contract. One of its first acts was
to acquire the Canada Central Railway, connecting
Ottawa and Pembroke, and other lines were bought giving
it access to Montreal. Consequently actual railway construction began at Pembroke in 1882, proceeding westward
up the Mattawa, following the voyageurs' route to Lake
Nipissing. From there the line cut across the courses of
southward-flowing streams to the north shore of Lake
Superior, which it followed to Fort William. It was here

20

the voyageurs had begun their portage from the St. Lawrence watershed to the headwaters of streams flowing into Hudson Bay.

This was the section about which there was most doubt. The route lay across a rockbound wilderness which seemed forever unlikely to provide traffic for a railway. Might not a stretch of line so expensive to build and operate prove too much for the rest of the railway to carry? No one suspected that it would ever become worthwhile for its own sake.

Once Lake Nipissing was left behind there was no parallel waterway along which supplies and equipment might be distributed to the construction crews. These must be hauled across country with horses over "tote" roads. The building of these roads across the Canadian Shield, with its rocky ridges, its many lakes and streams, and its stretches of muskeg, was in itself a considerable undertaking.

By the end of 1882 trains were running to Lake Nipissing; and by the end of the following year a further one hundred miles had been completed. Early in that year the tote road had reached the spot where Sudbury now stands, and with it the advance guard of right-of-way slashers. The core of a small community was soon established in a little clearing cut out of the bush. A log building was put up for the company's store and another to serve as a boarding house. Among the first arrivals were Dr. William H. Howey and his wife. They came from Delhi, Ontario, and had just recently been married. The Howeys were to spend the rest of their lives in Sudbury.

Many years afterward (1933), when the doctor was in his grave, Mrs. Howey, now within three years of her own death, wrote a book, *Pioneering on the C.P.R.*, in which she recounted some of her experiences during those days of railway construction. In March, 1883, travelling on a work train, she had arrived at Sturgeon Falls, a village on Sturgeon River a short distance above the point where it empties into Lake Nipissing. That little community, like

Mattawa, farther east, had been for many years a Hudson's Bay Company's post and was also a logging centre. The doctor, engaged at a salary of $75 a month to minister to ailing construction workers, had arrived some time previously.

Railway construction requires successive centres of activity. Each begins in a small way, as camps are set up ahead of construction to accommodate survey parties and those engaged in cutting out the right-of-way. With the approach of the grading crews, each in turn reaches its peak of population, quickly subsiding as the tracks pass on.

The Howeys' headquarters were to be first at "the Veuve" (River), the next centre west of Sturgeon Falls; but since their cabin was not yet ready they remained at Sturgeon Falls for three weeks till word came through that it was in a condition to shelter them.

Mrs. Howey went to the company's store at Sturgeon Falls and bought a few bits of furniture consisting of "a wooden bedstead, six Windsor chairs, and some good strong delft dishes." These were loaded onto a sleigh and sent on ahead, while the Howeys followed in the doctor's cariole, bumping over the tote road.

They discovered that their new home was built of logs which had only recently been growing as trees. The bark had been left on the outside, but inside the logs had been hewn smooth. Chinks between the logs were stuffed with moss. There were four rooms—living-room, bedroom, kitchen and office; but the house was still without doors, and the doctor hung blankets over the openings.

The Veuve was only their temporary home; toward the end of June, they were informed that a house being built for them in Sudbury was ready. By this time the track had gone past the Veuve and the end of steel was at Markstay, about a dozen miles to the west. So they packed their effects once more and Mrs. Howey, sitting on a bale of hay, travelled to Markstay on a flatcar, which also carried her household effects, while the doctor went ahead in his buckboard.

At Markstay the household effects were transferred to a
lumber wagon for the final twenty-four miles to Sudbury,
and the doctor and Mrs. Howey made the trip in the buckboard. "The tote road followed the right-of-way up hill
and down dale," Mrs. Howey wrote. "We jogged along
over long stretches of corduroy, bounded and bumped over
stones and roots, getting pretty tired and hot." They
reached their new home as the sun was setting on the first
of July, 1883.

The grade was at Sudbury that autumn, and in the
following March the first train arrived. Set as it was
among a confusion of rocky hills, Sudbury gave little
promise of becoming an important place. In fact, its
location was a matter of pure chance. The intention had
been to build the railway south of a lake of irregular shape
lying in an east-west position, about four miles long by one
mile at its greatest width, but the location engineer for
some unexplained reason ran the line north of it. It was
then called Lost Lake; but James Worthington, superintendent of construction for that part of the line, gave it
the name of the engineer who had made this error, and as
Lake Ramsay it has been known to generations of Sudburians, many of whom live along its shore.

In 1929, the Canadian Board on Geographical Names
at Ottawa learned that the proper spelling of the location
engineer's name was "Ramsey," not "Ramsay," and
changed the lake's name in accordance.[1] Another reason
was that there was another Lake Ramsay a short distance
farther west and the change was made to avoid confusion.
It seems a pity that the spelling of the latter was not
altered instead, for it is in a relatively uninhabited place
and the change could have been effected with very little
inconvenience to anyone. But, as matters stand, most
of the people of Sudbury are unaware of the new spelling
and will doubtless continue for years to spell the name of
their lake as they have always done, while the few who
know of the change will spell it differently.

[1]This information was received too late to change the spelling in this book.

Sudbury itself also owes its name to Worthington, who called it after the birthplace in Sussex, England, of his first wife. With a station to be named every few miles, there was no particular significance in Worthington's having chosen a name so intimately connected with his own family, and certainly there was nothing at that time to suggest that Sudbury would ever become much more than an unimportant way-station.

During its brief spell of activity as the chief centre of construction until a new centre had been established at Biscotasing, eighty-eight miles to the west, Sudbury reached its peak, but with the passing of the end of steel the population quickly dwindled. The place might have been almost deserted, if in the interval an incident had not occurred that was to play a vital part in its future.

About three miles beyond Sudbury, as the right-of-way was being cleared, a blacksmith named Tom Flanagan noticed a ridge consisting of heavily stained rocks. He dug a few holes in it and found copper sulphate. When the grading crew arrived, Flanagan's ridge was cut through and a considerable deposit of mineralized rock was laid bare.

It does not seem that Flanagan derived any benefit from his discovery, for a few months later the ground was acquired by others. On February 25, 1884 an application to purchase the property, consisting of Lot 11 in the fifth concession of McKim township, was made to the Department of Crown Lands of Ontario by Thomas and William Murray of Pembroke, Henry Abbott of Brockville, and John Loughrin of Mattawa.

This became the Murray mine, but was not operated by those who took out the patent, nor by anyone else until the property was bought by H. H. Vivian & Co. of Swansea, Wales, who, in 1889, undertook the first mining operations. The Vivians failed, but the mine has produced millions of dollars for its subsequent owners.

Even before Thomas Flanagan was attracted by the highly stained rocks of the ridge, the possibility of valuable ore had been considered. In the autumn of 1883, Andrew

McNaughton, the newly arrived stipendiary magistrate, had gone into the hills for a walk and lost his way. Parties were organized to search for him and one of these, which included Dr. Howey, found him sitting on a small knoll. Dr. Howey's inquiring eye was caught by the copper-stained appearance of the rocks upon which the tired magistrate was sitting. He chipped off a number of samples and a short while later showed them to Dr. Alfred Selwyn, Director of the Geological Survey of Canada, who was visiting Sudbury in company with Dr. Girdwood, head of the railway's medical services.

Much to Dr. Howey's disappointment, Dr. Selwyn, after careful examination, informed him that the iron sulphide comprising a large part of his samples was practically worthless, since the only metal of importance it might contain was nickel, and similar ores in other parts of the country did not contain enough of this metal to permit of profitable extraction. And as for the copper sulphide, Dr. Selwyn was of the opinion that it too was not present in sufficient quantity to justify the cost of mining. Dr. Howey threw his samples away; but afterwards, when the Murray mine had become a success, he was most scathing in his remarks about expert geological opinion.

In the meantime the grade had moved relentlessly on. A mile or two beyond the site of the future mine it passed through a zone of somewhat higher granitic hills opening out upon what seemed to be a flat upland valley covered, like the rest of the country, with heavy timber, chiefly white pine. The line continued in a north-westerly direction across this valley for about ten miles, passing out of it through another zone of high granitic hills similar to those which formed its southern boundary.

Within this valley, which appeared to be the bed of an inter- or post-glacial lake, stations were established at Azilda, Chelmsford and Larchwood which quickly became lumbering centres. When the timber was removed, the land proved fertile and soon was settled upon. Most of those who worked in the lumber camps and later took up

the land were *Canadiens*[1] who had come with the construction crews but preferred logging and farming, to which
they were more accustomed.

Before the railway came, timber in the forest which
once covered the whole country north of Lake Huron had
been cut and floated down the streams to Georgian Bay,
most of it being rafted across the lake to mills in Michigan.
Timber in the region around what later became Sudbury
had been taken out chiefly by way of the Spanish River
on the west, and by the Wanapitei on the east. Some in
Sudbury's immediate vicinity was floated down Junction
Creek, but when the railway arrived most of the timber was
still standing. For some time after the track moved on,
the C.P.R. maintained a timber-framing unit at Sudbury,
and after 1886 the mines provided a local market.

Sudbury was a convenient outfitting centre for the
lumber camps while cutting continued farther north, and
the merchants did well while the traffic lasted. For a few
weeks in spring, when the crews were paid off and until the
shantymen had spent their money, Sudbury saloons did a
thriving business. As late as 1903, seventeen lumber
companies were active in Sudbury district, employing more
than 11,000 men in the mills and bush.

But it was neither lumbering nor the railway that was to
convert Sudbury into an important community. It was the
stained rocks that had attracted the attention of Thomas
Flanagan and Dr. Howey. However, as the steel worked
its way westward, leaving Sudbury far behind, no one
dreamt of what the future was to bring.

[1]This spelling is used to denote Canadians of French descent.

# IV

# *Frontier Community*

WHEN THE CONSTRUCTION CREWS MOVED on, the straggling collection of shanties called Sudbury, so recently the scene of rush and bustle, became a ghost town. The fifteen hundred persons who for a short time had called it home had been reduced to three hundred men and a few women.

Mrs. Howey thought the wife of James Perkins, the walking boss, "a little doll of a woman." There were the wife of James McCormick, proprietor of the new Balmoral Hotel, and the three McCormick girls, Mollie, Susie and Nellie. There was also Miss Boyd, the telegraph operator, soon to become the bride of J. C. Worthington, son of the superintendent of construction. Mrs. Kilby, a dressmaker, had arrived with her two daughters, Edna and Mamie, who in due course married local bachelors and became the mothers of Sudburians. Josiah Smith brought his wife and family from Petawawa; and that summer Andrew McNaughton, the new stipendiary magistrate, arrived from Newcastle, Ontario, with his wife and four daughters, Elizabeth, Annie, Jessie and Jane, some of whose names still adorn streets in Sudbury.

Mrs. Howey intimates that there were other women whom she did not know, and one can imagine these proscribed females furtively plying their ancient profession, their presence ostentatiously ignored by their more fortunate sisters. From time to time, in years to come, attempts

27

would be made to get rid of them, but these would never quite succeed, for there was a belief, obstinately held, that they "brought business to a town."

Where had these people come from who were thus thrown together to found a city? Mostly they had come along with the railway in some capacity, and for one reason or another had decided that here they should tarry awhile. Most were Canadian-born, a large percentage French-speaking, while a few were immigrants of British stock, although as early as 1884 the first Ukrainians and Finns had arrived.

Many were from towns along the railway to the east— Renfrew, Pembroke, Mattawa—and during the next few years, as word of the prospects of this new western town drifted back to the towns in the Ottawa Valley, others came, some with families, to become Sudbury's pioneers. Their names persist among its leading citizens to this day. R. Dorsett and Charles Labelle, who arrived from Pembroke to establish a painting and decorating business, were typical of many others.

Robert Burns, having come with the railway as part-time storekeeper, later to marry Susan McCormick, handed out the mail as part of his duties for the C.P.R. When he shortly resigned to open a liquor store, Stephen Fournier, destined to become one of the town's best-known pioneers, became Sudbury's first official postmaster.

Jean-Etienne Fournier, born at Trois Pistoles, Quebec, had also come with the railway, after serving as store-keeper at a number of places farther east. A year later, he launched into business for himself, for the next few years changing frequently from one site to another, and from one business to another, but each time the post office moved with him.

At Sudbury the railway runs approximately north and south. A short distance to the east ran the tote road, and the stretch between the two creeks was Sudbury's first street. Instead of crossing the creek to the north, the road turned west along the concession line, over the tracks and up the hill.    The railway's store stood where the road made the turn, now the corner of Elm and Durham streets.

The first Catholic priests to arrive bought land on the north side of the creek (called Nolin, after Father J. B. Nolin, the first priest) outside the C.P.R.'s townsite. There they built a church and other buildings, and when Stephen Fournier moved from the C.P.R. property he bought a piece of land from them upon which he built a combined store and dwelling.   Fournier remained at this spot for two or three years and then built a store at the corner of Elm and Elgin streets.   It was known as the Golden Ball, because it had such an ornament on the roof.

Dr. and Mrs. Howey lived in a cottage perched on the brow of the hill, facing down the slope, at a spot now in the middle of Elm Street.   Farther down the hill, on the south side of the street, the company built a frame building for a hospital, and beyond that, on the opposite side, was the company's boarding house, later to become the Balmoral Hotel.   Dan Dunn's boarding house was on the same side of the street near the corner, across from the company's store.

John Frawley started a store in a tent on the north side of what was then the main street (now Elm), just west of Dunn's boarding house, and was shortly joined by "Bob" Tough, who contributed $488 in capital and another tent, but Tough soon deserted storekeeping for prospecting.   In 1899, John Frawley's brother, P. S., came from St. Louis to join him, and when a little later the firm dissolved, P. S. opened a more permanent type of store on the south side of Elm, near Durham, in 1907 moving to the corner since associated with the Frawley name.

Alex Tough opened the town's first pool hall, and Zotique Mageau, afterwards a member of the legislature, the first shoe store, both in tents.   But Pat Manion, whose son Robert was one day to lead a national political party, housed his men's wear store in a frame shack.   George Tuddenham, Sudbury's first barber, was to become one of its most active citizens.

The C.P.R. built its station, a two-storey structure with a single-storey baggage room attached, opposite the spot where the King Edward Hotel was later built. To represent the company and serve the citizens came C. J. Rea, the first agent, and with him as telegrapher C. W. Waggner. The company also built a long frame structure farther north on the same side of the track for company offices and the agent's residence. Here also was the office of Magistrate McNaughton.

After the telegraph office was moved into the company's new building, the little shack formerly used became the first schoolhouse and also served as a church building for non-Catholics.

A court house and gaol were soon necessary and a small frame house, distinguished from most because it was painted, was built on the slope to the south and east of the Howeys' cottage. The court house, the first public building, was used for many purposes, especially concerts and religious services.

Although two creeks more or less marked the boundaries of the community, the people got their drinking water from a spring that came out of the ground in a gravel pit where Athletic Park was afterwards laid out. Some took their own pails to the spring, but most of Sudbury's families were supplied by a man named Perras, who undertook to keep their barrels filled for twenty-five cents a barrel. After a few years, when well-drillers arrived, some of the hotels and other large users of water had wells put down.

The C.P.R. controlled the community, and only such businesses as it chose to allow could operate. By act of parliament (Public Works Act), no liquor could legally be sold while the railway was under construction, but there was considerable bootlegging. When the steel had passed to the westward and the interdiction against liquor was lifted, a number of taverns were opened. One of the first of these was the former C.P.R. boarding house, now known as the Balmoral Hotel, operated by James McCormick.

In 1887 the C.P.R. sent J. L. Morris, O.L.S., of Pembroke to survey the townsite. Someone decided that the streets running north and south should be named after governors-general, and the streets running east and west after trees. Thereafter the principal east and west street became Elm, and the principal north and south street Durham.

The first street north of Elm was called Beech, while to the south were Cedar and Larch. The street next to Durham on the west (running parallel to the railway tracks) was called Elgin, and the one next on the east Lisgar, with Young beyond. Although the map showed many more streets, Elm and Durham, with a street or two on either side, comprised the community for some years to come.

Sudbury still made but a small gap in the surrounding forest. Only the streets actually in use were yet cut out and the first task in putting up a new building was to clear the site of its timber. Not only was the settlement closely hedged on all sides by woods, but it was ringed about by granitic hills. Streets abruptly ended when one of these was encountered.

The streets themselves, except where they traversed patches of exposed rock, were quagmires after each rainfall, and traffic along them was further impeded by huge stumps, many of which, cut off at what was once the level of the roadway, remained as traffic hazards for years.

Sudbury occupied the central portion of the township of McKim, in the electoral district of Nipissing, and as soon as the community took on a semblance of permanency a township council was organized and an enrolment of property-holders was undertaken to determine who should have the vote. Similar councils were organized in Azilda, Chelmsford, Larchwood and other nearby communities. James McCormick was the first reeve of McKim township.

Cut off as the people were from contact with the rest of the province, division of opinion along political lines scarcely existed, but religious differences were well marked, and these were carried over into municipal affairs. Consequently, municipal offices were filled on a basis of religion, and thus James McCormick, the first reeve, and Stephen Fournier, who succeeded him and for several years was regularly re-elected, were both Catholics. That the vote was based on religion rather than nationality is shown by the fact that often as many as three of the four councillors were Irish Catholics.

Sudbury's first doctors were in the employ of the railway. Some moved on with the construction crews, but William H. Howey and R. B. Struthers remained in Sudbury for the rest of their days. Both were active in public affairs, although Howey only once held an elective office. Howey dearly loved a joke, and numerous anecdotes concerning him are still being recounted, but most of them, upon investigation, are found to have been told also about doctors elsewhere. Nevertheless, he was undoubtedly an inveterate joker, a genial, friendly man beloved of all. When not actually caring for a patient he could usually be found in Herb Young's drugstore, where he, Arthur Storrie, the police officer, and others who liked a joke were in the habit of gathering.

Although a frontier community, Sudbury had the distinction of having one of the first, if not the first, woman doctor in Canada. For many years, Helen E. R. Ryan, wife of the township's first clerk, conducted a medical practice there. Born Helen E. Reynolds, her home before her marriage was in Forest, Ontario.

Another doctor who was to spend the remainder of his life in Sudbury was W. H. Mulligan, who arrived in 1889 and two years later opened the first drug store and pharmacy.

Among early lawyers were G. E. K. Cross and F. F. Lemieux. The former moved to North Bay, but Lemieux remained to become a well-known figure and was several times mayor.

Because of the large proportion of *Canadien* families, Roman Catholicism was the first religious denomination to become established. Like the people he helped, Father

Nolin came with the construction crews, but remained in Sudbury and began the building of a permanent religious settlement. Application was made to the provincial government for the purchase of Lot 5, Concession IV, immediately to the north of Elm Street.

Mrs. Howey mentions the Rev. Gowan Gillmor as the first Anglican minister she met in Sudbury, while the Rev. James Lohore was the first Presbyterian missionary in the district. The Methodists had a church on Beech Street in 1886, presided over by student missionaries.

Two things which served to prevent Sudbury from remaining a mere whistle stop on the railway were the decision of the C.P.R. to build a branch to Sault Ste. Marie and later one to Toronto, and the discovery of mineral deposits.

The incorporation of the Canadian Copper Company in 1886 made money available for mining development and provided an incentive for prospectors to continue their search for mineral outcrops. But the company had soon acquired as much property as it could reasonably expect to work, and many prospectors were left with good properties which they could not sell and for which they could not secure money needed for development.

This led to an agitation for the establishment of a custom smelter so that prospectors might have their ore smelted and thus find a market for it. The project became practically a civic enterprise; the organizing committee was headed by Reeve Fournier and most of the principal business men of the village and surrounding district were associated with it. Eventually a company was organized with an authorized capital of $75,000, and efforts were made to have the capital subscribed. The provincial government was approached (unsuccessfully) for assistance, and the support of the Toronto Board of Trade was enlisted.

Despite the efforts of the promoters, only a few thousand dollars was subscribed, and the company was finally wound up, subscriptions (except those made by the provisional directors) being returned. In the light of later experience, it is not likely that the scheme would have worked if the stock had been sold and the smelter built. The time was soon to come when the district would have many extinct smelters. Furthermore, the nickel industry did not lend itself to small-scale operations. At that time, even the Canadian Copper Company, with its wealthy backers, was not having an easy time.

Another public matter which engaged the time and efforts of many of the leading citizens was the agitation against the proposal of the Mowat government to impose a royalty upon mineral production. In this campaign Æneas McCharles, James Stobie and J. B. Hammond, all prospectors, took a leading part. They objected strenuously to the imposition of any royalty, and advocated changes in the mining regulations which would prevent the tying up of mining lands by large companies without their being required to spend any money in development.

This agitation extended over a number of years, resulted in countless letters to the newspapers and a number of deputations to wait upon the government. The policy of imposing a royalty was deferred and later dropped, and with this the prospectors were forced to be content; but there would be other issues.

In other ways, the growth of a community spirit was becoming evident, and in none perhaps more so than in the realm of sport. From the outset curling was a favourite pastime, while in summer lacrosse attracted the younger Sudburians. In each case challenges were issued to clubs in Mattawa, North Bay, Chapleau and the Soo. Within a short time suitable trophies had been provided.

Sudbury was getting old enough to take note of the death of an "old-timer" in the person of Andrew Mc-Naughton, Magistrate since 1883, who died April 24, 1892. He had been a charter member of Nickel Lodge of the Masonic Order, whose members turned out in force to escort the remains to the station after a Masonic ceremony conducted by Dr. Howey. The body was shipped to Newcastle for interment.

Sudbury Soon After It Became a Town

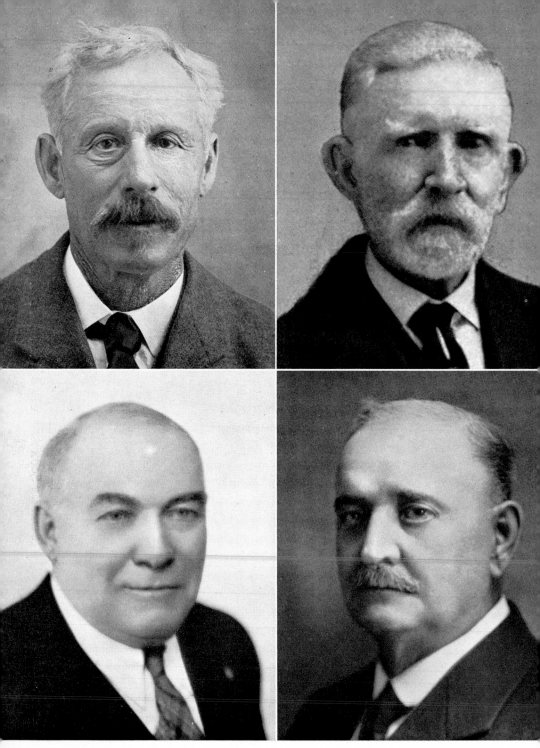

Thomas Baycroft

Russell Cryderman

Francis C. Crean

Wm. McVittie

At the meeting on December 31, 1891, when what was to prove the last nominations for Reeve and Councillors for the township of McKim, including Sudbury, were made the division of the citizens along religious lines had been more evident than ever. Two slates had been proposed. One, calling itself "The People's Candidates," contained the names of Stephen Fournier for Reeve and Messrs. D. O'Connor, Jos. Anctil, J. C. McCormack and A. Gallagher for Councillors. The other, which called itself "The People's Ticket," was headed by Gus Harwood, nominated for Reeve, and Messrs. R. Martin, A. McIntyre, D. L. McKinnon and James Potter for Councillors. The elections, held on January 4th, resulted in a victory for Stephen Fournier and the rest of his slate by large majorities.

# V

# *Glint of Gossan*

SUDBURY'S FIRST PROSPECTOR IS NOT known. There were probably several in such a community who had done some prospecting before, but discovery of Sudbury ores was due to none of these. It was an accident, as already told, and at the time caused little stir. Tom Flanagan discovered copper sulphides along the C.P.R. right-of-way in August, 1883, but it was not till the following February that application was made to the Ontario government for permission to buy the land upon which the mineral deposit was found. And the applicants were not residents of Sudbury. Thomas and William Murray were merchants of Pembroke, Henry Abbott lived at Brockville, and the fourth partner, John Loughrin, was a merchant of Mattawa. Since Loughrin had a tie contract with the railway, it is probable that he induced the others to join him in the venture. The sum involved was $310, for 310 acres of land. Little did this venturesome four realize that some day millions of dollars would be taken from that parcel of land!

Doubtless the general feeling was that, despite their rich hues, the rocks contained no other riches. Had not Dr. Howey received such assurance from no less a person than Dr. Selwyn, head of the Geological Survey of Canada?

Such an opinion might have satisfied Dr. Howey, but it did not deter the prospectors who, strangely enough, had not previously known anything about prospecting. Neither were they deterred by the fact that a more difficult terrain to prospect could scarcely have been found. No roads or trails existed and men must carry on their backs what in other countries might be packed on horses or burros. Canoes could be used in places, but only to explore the margins of lakes. Navigable streams did not flow in the right directions. Rugged, timber-covered hills were divided by valleys filled with swamps which in spring were too full of water to traverse on foot and too shallow for canoes. The short summer season was shortened still further by periods during which flies and mosquitoes made bush-travel a torment.

Every mining camp seems to produce at least one colourful figure, and in Sudbury that man undoubtedly was Rinaldo McConnell. Formerly a timber cruiser, the stained rocks of Sudbury Basin so stained his imagination that prospecting came to occupy more and more of his time and attention. From the first his faith in the value and importance of the nickel range (not then understood as such) was complete, and either as prospector or middleman he had a hand in most of the big deals in Sudbury's early years.

As a prospector, he could hold his own with any in finding his way through the bush, fighting flies and mosquitoes, and searching out the hidden lairs of mineral deposits. If need be, he could open up a mine and operate it. But, as a salesman, he was superb. Many millions of dollars came to Sudbury directly or indirectly through his efforts.

Francis Charles Crean afterwards claimed that he was the first to see evidence of copper ore in the ballast of the C.P.R. tracks west of Sudbury, and at any rate he was the first to make application for a mining claim. In those days staking was not necessary. Most of the territory about Sudbury was already surveyed into townships and lots, and all the prospector need do was to locate the lot he wished to acquire and make application to the Department

of Crown Lands at Toronto. The application was usually
accompanied by an affidavit that the applicant, or his
agent, had found what seemed to be a mineral deposit, but
this was not always required.

Townships varied somewhat in size, but were usually
six miles square, each subdivided into seventy-two lots,
ranged in six tiers, called "concessions," of twelve lots each,
and each lot was therefore one mile long (north and south)
by half a mile wide, containing approximately 320 acres.

Francis Crean's application, covering the south half of
lot 12 in the fifth concession of McKim township, later
known as the Elsie mine, was dated May 9, 1884. For some
reason the patent was not issued until 1888 and was then
made over to Crean's nominee, Henry Totten, who later
sold to the Lake Superior Power Company of Sault Ste.
Marie.

Crean was busy that spring of 1884. In addition to the
Elsie, he discovered the prospect which became the
Worthington mine. Copper ore in the ballast of the
C.P.R.'s Soo line, about twenty-five miles southwest of
Sudbury, led Crean to apply for the purchase of a tract still
within the limits of a timber berth which when surveyed
a few weeks later became part of lot 2, concession 2, in
Drury township. The property was later acquired by the
Dominion Mineral Company of which James Worthington,
after whom the mine was named, was a director and large
shareholder.

Crean made several other discoveries in the same year.
One was on the north half of lot 1, concession 2, and
another on the north half of lot 2, concession 1, both in
Drury township, for which application to purchase was
made by Henry Totten. The first was afterwards known
as the Howland mine, and the second the Totten prospect.

Crean was also the discoverer of the Crean Hill mine,
named after himself, on the south half of lot 5, concession 5,
of Denison township. It was a steady producer for many
years, its ore containing a higher percentage of copper than
nickel rendering it suitable for mixing with Creighton ore.

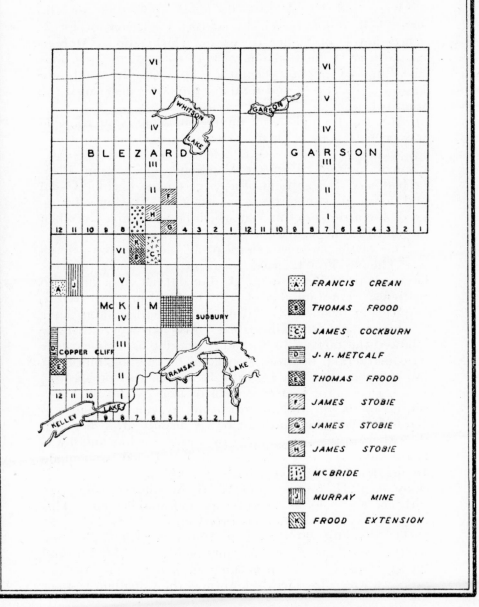

*Plan showing township survey and mining claims in McKim and Blezard located by early prospectors.*

McConnell was not far behind Crean. On May 16, 1884, he and Joseph Riopelle made application for the south half of lot 1 and the southeast quarter of lot 2, concession 4, of Snider township, which adjoins McKim on the west. These claims were transferred to the Canadian Copper Company when it was later organized and were known as its Nos. 4 and 6 mines, the latter also called the Clarabelle mine.

McConnell employed a number of scouts and Riopelle was probably one of them. Henri Ranger was another of his scouts, in some ways as colourful a character as McConnell himself. Born at Vaudreuil, Quebec, in 1845, he had served as captain of a barge on the Lachine Canal and for a time had been a farmer at Mattawa before becoming a timber cruiser at which he was employed when he joined in the search for gossan showings.

One of the most successful of all the early prospectors was Thomas Frood. Like many other Sudbury pioneers he was born at Renfrew (1843), but did not come direct to Sudbury. For a number of years he lived in southwestern Ontario, in business as a druggist at Southampton, later teaching school near Kincardine. Also like many others he followed the railway to Sudbury, working as a timekeeper on construction, but was soon lured by the possibilities of prospecting. On May 18, 1884, he and another prospector, James Cockburn, located a vein of iron pyrites on lot 7, concession 6, of McKim township, tracing the outcrop across the boundary into lot 6. A dispute arose between the two as to the ownership of the respective lots and 6 was finally allocated to Cockburn and 7 to Frood, who made application for the south half. Cockburn transferred his claim to J. H. Metcalf and W. B. McAllister, who were early in the field as prospectors and middlemen. This property became the famous Frood mine.

On November 20, 1884, J. H. Metcalf filed an application for the west half of lot 12, concession 3, of McKim, and the east half of lot 1, concession 3, of Snider. The McKim property was subsequently known as the Canadian Copper

Company's McArthur, or No. 2 mine, while the parcel in Snider, called the McAllister mine after Metcalf's partner, had its name changed to the Lady Macdonald mine, following a visit from the Prime Minister's wife in 1886.

During all this time the prospectors followed the only clue they knew. They had discovered that a showing of gossan was a good indication of copper ore. It was always associated with one particular type of rock, which they called "diorite," later found to be norite. As yet no geologist had examined the area and no geological mapping had been done. The extent of the mineralized area was still unknown.

By the spring of 1885 many new prospectors had joined in the search, and those who had spent the previous year in the bush were still eager to take the trail. Thomas Frood was early in the field, working in association with Metcalf and McAllister. He located mineral on the north half of lot 12, concession 2, of McKim. This, an offset deposit, became known as the Copper Cliff mine, from the gossan-covered hill which marked it, and eventually the site of the Canadian Copper Company's smelting works.

Metcalf and McAllister were busy in other parts of the field. On July 10, 1885, they put in an application for several lots in the townships of Denison, Creighton and Snider. One of these, the north half of lot 10, concession 1, of Creighton township was to become the site of the great Creighton mine, but it is doubtful if the applicants had then any idea that it even contained an ore deposit. Since it was not necessary to stake properties applied for, and applicants were not always required to declare the presence of mineral, the presumption is that they made a blanket application covering property which, from the proximity of other discoveries, they thought might be mineral-bearing.

One new man in 1885 was James Stobie, who was to discover some of the most important mining properties in the Sudbury field. Born in Perth, Scotland, in 1840, he had been brought to Canada as a child, his family living at Ottawa, where he grew up. Although for some years he spent the greater part of his time in Sudbury, where he was active in all matters connected with mining, he made his home at Portlock, near Sault Ste. Marie.

In August, 1885, Stobie discovered the Mount Nickel mine, on the south half of lot 5, concession 2, of the township of Blezard, and later in the same year, the south half of lot 5, concession 1, of the same township. The latter, for which application was made jointly by Stobie and Mc-Connell, has since been known as the Stobie mine, an early producer. In the same month Stobie also discovered what is known as the Little Stobie mine on the north half of lot 6, concession 1, of Blezard township.

Another discovery of the year 1885 was what became known as the Evans mine, on the south half of lot 1, concession 2, of Snider township, made by F. J. Eyre.

As yet no actual mining had been undertaken anywhere in Sudbury Basin. The first mines would be opened in the coming year and it would be two years longer before the first smelter would be blown in.

Henri Ranger was one of the most active prospectors in 1886. He discovered evidences of copper on lots 8, 11 and 12, concession 4, of Denison township, and on the north half of lot 1 and the south halves of lots 6, 8 and 9, concession 5, of the same township. Ranger assigned his interest to Rinaldo McConnell and nominees of the latter. These properties later constituted the McConnell mine, subsequently known as the Victoria.

Having finished scouting for McConnell, Ranger set out to prospect on his own account. He succeeded in locating mineral on the north half of lot 10, concession 1, Creighton township, but when he applied for the property was informed that Metcalf and McAllister had applied for this parcel among others on August 10, 1885. Patent had not yet been applied for by the previous applicants and it was not till January 24, 1887, that it was issued to the Canadian Copper Company, nominee of the applicants. In view of the subsequent value of the property, there was a feeling in some quarters that Ranger had been discriminated against in favour of a large corporation, but the procedure seems to have been in accordance with existing regulations. No staking was required, mining lands could be bought for one dollar an acre, and priority of application was what counted most.

Henri Ranger was active again in 1887, on September 3rd discovering gold and copper on lot 6, concession 4, of Denison township. His interest was transferred to Robert J. Tough, who applied for a patent covering also lot 5, and patent was issued to him on October 9th of that year. This became known as the Vermilion mine. It was in a class by itself. First regarded as a gold mine, several thousand dollars' worth of gold was taken from it. The nickel and copper content of its ore was unusually high, and it was also rich in platinum and palladium.

The first discovery in what is now Falconbridge township, then still classed as timber land, was made in November, 1887, by Richard S. Donally, a woods ranger in the employ of the Emery Lumber Company, who held the timber rights. Because of objections on the part of his employers Donally did not apply for the mineral rights until 1890 when, to forestall others, application was made and the patent issued in the names of Donally, John Paterson and the Emery Lumber Company. The claim was later surveyed as M. 2.

Most of the regular prospectors were still searching for outcrops farther west. In October, 1887, Michael Corrigan discovered ore on the west half of lot 12, concession 2, of Denison, generally known as the Robinson prospect and patented to Corrigan and Hiram Robinson the following April. What became known as the McIntyre mine, on lot 11, concession 3, of Denison township, was patented to David L. Lockerby on January 3, 1888. Another small deposit on the south rim, lot 1, concession 3, Blezard township, was patented to Thos. H. Sheppard, June 12, 1890, and variously known as the Sheppard, Beatrice or Davis mine.

By this time the prospectors were working both westward and eastward. Benjamin Boyer, prospecting for James B. Miller, of Sault Ste. Marie, applied for lot 3, concession 5, of Drury township on June 20, 1889. This property, known as the Chicago, Travers or Inez mine, was worked for a short while but was not among the successful ones.

What was to become an important mine was located on April 30, 1891, by John T. Cryderman, who found a large showing of gossan amid standing pine on the southern parts of lots 4 and 5, concession 3, of Garson township. Known for a time as the Cryderman mine, it has since been known as the Garson, steadily producing since 1908.

A group of claims in the west end of the Basin were located by Benjamin Boyer in 1891 on behalf of James B. Miller, who transferred them to the Great Lakes Copper Company. These included the Sultana, on the south half of lot 8, and the southwest quarter of lot 7, concession 1, of Trill township, and lots 6 and 7, concession 6, of Drury.

In August, 1892, Alexander McKay made a discovery on the north half of the northeast quarter of lot 11, concession 4, of Trill, which also became the property of the Great Lakes Copper Company. Later, the north half of the southeast quarter and the south half of the northeast quarter of lot 11, concession 4 of Trill were patented to the Great Lakes Copper Company in consequence of discoveries made by Alexander McKay, the patent having been held up in the meantime because of a dispute.

What was later known as the Trillabelle or Gillespie mine was discovered by Ralph Gillespie in September, 1891, on the northwest quarter of lot 10 and the northeast quarter of lot 11, concession 3, of Trill.

Earlier in the same year, Daniel O'Connor had secured a patent covering lot 12, concession 3, of Denison township. This was later known as the Gersdorffite mine but has never been brought under production.

The Cameron mine, on lot 7, concession 1, of Blezard was discovered in August, 1892, by Robert McBride. It was named after Ian Cameron, manager of the Blezard mine owned by the Dominion Mineral Company, with whom McBride was associated.

William McVittie and George Jackson discovered the Kirkwood mine on the south half of lot 8, concession 3, of Garson township in 1892, leasing it to T. M. Kirkwood. In common with much of the country in the eastern end of the Basin at that time, the property was covered with pine timber. Although some ore has been taken from it, no serious attempt has ever been made to operate it.

McVittie and Jackson were also responsible for the location of what became the Gertrude mine on the south portions of lots 3, 4 and 5, concession 1, of Creighton. This property was later acquired by the Clergue interests of Sault Ste. Marie and operated for a time.

On September 2, 1893, Thomas Baycroft discovered the Tam O'Shanter property, consisting of the northwest portion of lot 5 and the north half of lot 6, concession 3, of Snider township. The Canadian Copper Company later acquired the claims but they have never been developed.

Although surrounded by older locations, the south half of the southwest quarter of lot 9, concession 3, of Snider, remained open until September, 1898, when Æneas Mc-Charles made application for it, securing the patent, September 13, 1899. Known as the North Star, McCharles sold it to the Mond Nickel Company in 1902, who operated it from time to time.

On November 21, 1900, patents were issued to John Moodie, covering lot 8, concession 4, to Henry R. Leyden for the northwest quarter of the south half of lot 7, and to Charles E. Ritchie for the north half of the north half of lot 7, all in concession 4 of Falconbridge township, and the south fifty-one and one-half acres of lot 7, concession 5, of the same township, based on discoveries made by J. T. Cryderman in November, 1898.

Between 1889 and 1891 a number of mineral deposits were located along the eastern rim of the Basin by several prospectors, including Rinaldo McConnell, Edgar J. Jarvis,

Robert Woods, John Watson, Charles E. Fitton, W. B. Poulson, James F. Whitson, John K. Leslie and George S. Macdonald, the property acquired by the latter being known as the Victor mine. None of these properties, however, has produced a mine of consequence. But the country is masked by overburden and the past is no criterion for the future.

More successful have been those who located properties along the north rim. In the autumn of 1887 James Stobie examined rock cuttings along the Canadian Pacific Railway's tracks between Larchwood and Cartier stations, finding likely-looking indications. But it was not till two years later that he located mineral outcrops on the south part of lot 7 and on lot 6, concession 2, of Levack, and on lot 2, concession 4. In the meantime, the deposit on the north half of lot 6 had been found by Indians prospecting for Rinaldo McConnell, who applied for and secured the patent. Stobie, however, secured the south three-quarters of lot 7. Held for some years by Stobie, McConnell and R. J. Tough, these claims finally became the property of the Mond Nickel Company and now constitute the Levack mine.

On the north parts of lots 2 and 3, respectively, concession 4, of Levack are the Big Levack and Strathcona properties. The former was discovered by James Stobie in 1889, while the latter was discovered by an Indian and patented to Thomas B. Ross and Donald C. MacTavish, employees of the Hudson's Bay Company, who called it after Lord Strathcona, their company's governor.

On July 24, 1889, at the angle of the north and east rims, Isaac Whistle and Arthur Belfeuille discovered a large gossan-covered area on the north part of lot 6, concession 4, of Norman township and the south part of lot 6, concession 5. This became the Whistle mine and an extension of the deposit on the southwest quarter of the north half of lot 5, concession 4, is known as the Wildcat mine.

Others who searched for gossan along the north rim were the Rangers—Xavier and Fred as well as Henri—

Ernest McBride, John T. Newton and Russell Cryderman. In the meantime, mining had begun at a number of points along the south rim, but the industry was far from flourishing. Prospectors had produced many more properties than there were capitalists with money to develop them. Those who did make sales received prices which in the light of later events were pitifully meagre.

William McVittie, who did not reach Sudbury till 1889, but shrewder than some of his fellow prospectors, made a number of sales at better prices and later invested his money in a power project on the Wanapitei which made him a millionaire. Rinaldo McConnell, who it is estimated received upward of three-quarters of a million dollars during his career, left a modest estate when he died. James Stobie was also fairly successful in disposing of prospects for considerable sums. He retired with a comfortable fortune and died in 1919 at Ypsilanti, Michigan.

Thomas Frood, whose name is associated with one of the greatest nickel mines in the world, did not remain long in Sudbury after prospects became scarce, making his home on the shore of the North Channel, across from Little Current, Manitoulin Island, where he lived with his second wife until he died in 1916. He was buried at Kincardine.

Francis C. Crean, who located the first prospect (or whose application bore the earliest date), did not continue to live at Sudbury after the principal exposures were filed upon. He spent his later years in Montreal, living to a ripe old age.

Æneas McCharles, who arrived in Sudbury in 1889, and whose principal discovery was the North Star mine, in his autobiography, *Bemocked of Fate*, lamented that his money had come too late to be of much use to him. Like Frood, a schoolteacher in early life, he was always concerned with the affairs of any community in which he lived. When the Ontario government proposed to levy a royalty on nickel production, he, James Stobie and J. B. Hammond waged a steady campaign against the proposal.

McCharles left ten thousand dollars to the University of
Toronto "on the following terms and conditions: namely,
That the interest therefrom shall be given from time to
time, but not necessarily every year, like the Nobel prizes
in a small way: (1) To any Canadian from one end of the
country to the other, and whether student or not, who
invents or discovers any new and improved process for the
treatment of Canadian ores or minerals of any kind, after
such process has been proved to be of special merit on a
practical scale; (2) or for any important discovery, invention
or device, by any Canadian, that will lessen the dangers
and loss of life in connection with the use of electricity in
supplying power and light; (3) or for any marked public
distinction achieved by any Canadian in scientific research
in any useful, practical line."

# VI

# *Every Step a Struggle*

IT WAS ONE THING TO LOCATE A PROSPECT, and quite another to find the money needed to make it into a mine. Before the ore could be converted into the products of commerce a complicated and expensive process was necessary. Since most of the deposits were in the form of outcrops, mining could be done by open-pit methods, much cheaper than if worked from a shaft, but the next step was costly.

Ores in the Sudbury district consisted mainly of combinations of sulphides of iron, copper and nickel, containing an average of four or five per cent combined nickel and copper in varying proportions, about forty per cent iron, and about thirty-five per cent sulphur. After rocky material had been removed by hand-sorting on belts and tables, the ore was taken by various means of transport to roast yards where much of the sulphur was removed by its own combustion. This was done by piling heaps of ore upon a foundation of cordwood sufficient to maintain a fire for about sixty hours. The burning cordwood ignited the sulphur, which then continued to burn, sometimes for three or four months or more, until all but ten or eleven per cent of the sulphur had been consumed.

From the roast yard the ore passed to the blast furnace, which removed further rocky matter, thereby increasing the proportions of copper and nickel in relation to the iron and sulphur. The product of this process was called "matte," consisting usually of about thirty-five per cent combined

49

nickel and copper, sometimes less. This was now "bessemer-ized" by adding quartz (or some other flux) to the matte in a special type of furnace, and forcing an air blast through the molten material. This caused the iron to combine with the silica in the quartz to form a slag on the surface of the molten charge which, after having been poured off, would leave a matte containing from seventy-five to eighty per cent nickel and copper, the balance being mostly sulphur and precious metals (gold, silver, platinum, palladium, etc.).

For two years prospectors had been locating mineral deposits with little hope of developing them. Most prospectors, for a grubstake or a little money to go on with, had already pledged a share of what they should find. There was no local capital. In fact, little capital for mining existed in Canada. Most wealthy men in Toronto, Ottawa and Montreal had made their money in the fur trade, in lumbering or in general merchandise. Latterly, some had made money in railway building and speculation, but that field was still lucrative, and railway money was not to be had for other purposes.

Furthermore, Canadian capitalists had had very little experience in mining ventures. Scarcely any heavy manu-facturing was yet being done, and no large market existed in Canada for metals. It was therefore quite natural that the first person to appreciate the possibilities of the Sudbury field should have been an American manufacturer and financier. He was Samuel J. Ritchie, of Cleveland, Ohio, who had first come to Ontario in search of second-growth hickory for his carriage factory at Akron, and had become interested in iron deposits in Hastings County.

Associated with Ritchie were several wealthy and influential Ohio men. After building a railway over which to ship his iron ore, Ritchie discovered that, because of its high sulphur content, the ore was not marketable, and he looked about for a venture that might enable him and his associates to recoup their losses.

While visiting William C. Van Horne, then general manager of the Canadian Pacific Railway, Ritchie was

STEPHEN FOURNIER

WILLIAM E. MASON

FRANK COCHRANE

CHARLES McCREA

shown samples of the ore taken from the rock-cut west of Sudbury by Thomas Tait, Van Horne's secretary. To Samuel Ritchie the presence of copper mines in Canada within a short distance of the Great Lakes had a definite meaning. He decided to investigate, with the result that thereafter his energies and resources were devoted to the development of Sudbury's mines.

Quietly he began acquiring the most likely prospects, and on January 6, 1886, the Canadian Copper Company, with an authorized capitalization of $2,000,000 (later increased to $2,500,000) was incorporated in Ohio to operate the properties acquired. At the same time the Anglo-American Iron Company, with identical shareholders, was incorporated to own and operate the properties in Hastings County. Ritchie was the first president, being succeeded in September, 1886, by Thomas W. Cornell, who occupied the position till January, 1891, when he was succeeded by "Judge" Stevenson Burke, who retained the position till 1902. In order to operate in Canada, the Canadian Copper Company applied for a special Act of Parliament, but continued to be an American company with its head office in Cleveland.

The first property acquired by Ritchie (in the name of the Anglo-American Iron Company) was the Crean Hill deposit, located by Francis C. Crean. Then came the purchase of the Frood and Stobie properties, and about the same time the deposits at Copper Cliff were secured. All but Crean Hill were bought by the Canadian Copper Company.

Mining was started on May 1, 1886, at the Copper Cliff mine, and later in the same year the Evans and Stobie mines were opened. L. H. Ashman was the first superintendent and John D. Evans the first engineer. Ore was shipped to England, to the continent of Europe, and to the United States.

The conditions at Sudbury in 1886 were disheartening [wrote D. H. Browne, a later official of the company]. The Algoma branch of the Canadian Pacific Railway, which had been built

five or six years before . . . had been abandoned.   This branch
from Sudbury to Copper Cliff was repaired so that trains could
run over it at the rate of eight miles an hour, and a corduroy road
was built from Sudbury to the Mines.   Work commenced in
May 1886 with 25 men on the payroll.   In December this had
risen to 65 men. . . . The Company's office was in Sudbury and
the Manager walked out and back to the mines.   What the mud
is like is shown by a letter from Frank Sperry, the chemist, telling
how he and Mr. Ashman had fished out the body of a boy who
was drowned in a hole in the road opposite the American Hotel
in Sudbury.   Mud and money were the main troubles, nearly
every letter from the Manager contains apologies for the payroll,
about $4,000 per month.   Mr. Ashman knows what trouble the
treasurer has to raise the necessary funds.

Freight was incredibly slow.   In June, 1887, Ashman
complains that five cars of ore have been standing in the Sudbury
yards for three weeks.   There was no side track from the railway
to the mines.   The large expense for freight caused the company
to look into the project of smelting the ores. . . .[1]

If the ore could be smelted at the mine, transportation
costs might be lessened considerably.   Building a smelter
at Copper Cliff would not be a difficult matter, but Ritchie
was not a metallurgist, and he engaged Dr. E. D. Peters, a
young American metallurgist, to make a study of the
situation.   Evidently Dr. Peters' report was satisfactory,
for according to Mr. Browne:

In 1888 Dr. Peters came up to Copper Cliff to pick out a site
for a roast yard and smelter.   The roast yard was staked out on
a clay flat, beside a little stream, which the beavers had dammed.
The beavers objected to the destruction of their waterworks and
repaired the dam by night as fast as it was torn away.   Exter-
mination of the beavers marked the triumph of the human mind.

In August, 1888, a roast pile was built and started burning in
the middle of a dense growth of spruce and birch trees.   Again
mind triumphed over matter and the woods fell before the stench.
The roast yard was quite a success.   In September, Peters
reports, "we have been putting 117 tons a day on the roast yard.
No man in America is heap-roasting half this amount of ore".

In November, 1888, the first furnace was erected.   It was a
Herreshoff water-jacket furnace, 6 feet long, three feet wide and
nine feet high.   It was built by the Nichols Chemical Company

---

[1]From an unpublished manuscript.

and shipped to the Jenks Manufacturing Company of Sherbrooke to be assembled. Their method of assembling showed more ingenuity than foresight, as will appear later.

Meanwhile a furnace building of frame, 40 feet long and 35 feet wide had been erected, and boilers and blowing engine installed. The work went very slowly. Peters in November explains in one of his letters that he had to send a man to North Bay, 80 miles, to cut and thread pipe. During this month Mr. H. P. McIntosh, the secretary-treasurer of the Canadian Copper Company, who seems to have been impressed with the future possibilities of the business, wrote to ask Dr. Peters if it would be possible to extend the plant to smelt 300 tons of ore a day. Dr. Peters replied that "he thinks we could do it but such large figures are rather bewildering". As to lighting the smelter by electricity, he says he has seen a number of electric lighting installations and in each case the thing was a dismal failure, and so advises against it. As to smelting, he says that 100 tons ore a day is enormous and almost unprecedented.

On December 22nd, 1888, the furnace with a crew of French-Canadians, who had never seen such a thing before, was fired up. The floor of the furnace room was flooded, and every time the furnace was tapped the explosions sounded like a gatling gun. McArthur, who had to do most of the work himself, had a platform slung above the settler, and on this were stationed two men with pails, to put out the fire on the roof that followed each tap. On December 25th, they had to stop work. McArthur's eyes were so badly burned that a boy was told off to lead him round. So they closed down and hunted for the trouble.

It appears that the bronze connection ring which fits between the furnace and the settler was the source of the disturbance. This ring was hollow and water-cooled. The Jenks Co. machinists having some difficulty in getting this onto the shell of the furnace had sawed it into four pieces, and fitted these together inside the iron work. With matte and slag running continuously over this split ring the only wonder is that any of the furnace-men lived to tell the tale. After considerable vituperative correspondence with Jenks, a new tapping ring was fitted, this time in one piece.

In January the furnace was started again and Dr. Peters was delighted to find that he could smelt from 80 to 100 tons of ore a day, producing a matte containing about 50% and a slag containing about $1\frac{1}{2}$ to 2% copper-nickel. This matte was shipped to H. H. Vivian of Wales; to Chas. Tennant of London; Wharton of Camden; with occasional shipments to Hamburg. During 1889 there was but 20 tons of matte shipped to the Orford Works.

In this year, 8,450 tons of matte was produced, containing 22.4% Cu., and 14.3% Ni., or 3,107 tons of nickel in matte. This was twice as much nickel as the entire world produced in 1888.   It piled up in the smelting yards and the problem of a market was still unsolved.

It was up to Ritchie to find the market.  His mind flashed back to a day in 1876 when he had met an eccentric Englishman named Gamgee, in Washington, D.C., who was studying yellow fever.   Gamgee had a theory that the fever could be cured by subjecting patients to near-freezing temperatures, and proposed building a hospital ship equipped with refrigeration chambers.  In attempting to devise such refrigeration equipment, he could find no metal that would withstand the corrosive action of ammonia.

Ritchie found Gamgee interesting and one day they visited the Smithsonian Institution together.   A meteorite with a large polished section attracted their attention, and upon questioning an attendant, they were told that it was a natural alloy of nickel and iron and extremely hard and tough.  It immediately occurred to Gamgee that here might be the material he was looking for and he began experimenting with nickel alloys.  He secured his nickel from Joseph Wharton, of Camden, at that time the only refiner of nickel in America, and eventually succeeded in getting an alloy containing eight per cent nickel.  Gamgee's scheme did not materialize, and he fades out of the story, but he did not fade from Ritchie's mind.

It occurred to Ritchie that in the manufacture of heavy guns and armour plate for naval ships, nickel might have a place.  He wrote to the Krupps, at Essen, Germany, telling of Gamgee's experiments and asking about the possibility of nickel being used in the Krupp works.  They did not treat the matter seriously, doubting that the limited supply of nickel would justify any extended experiments in its use. But as a result of Ritchie's efforts the matter was referred to the Iron and Steel Institute of Great Britain, which appointed one of its members, James Riley, of Glasgow, to try some experiments with nickel as an alloy for steel. Riley's report, in May, 1889, confirmed Ritchie's claims.

Armed with a copy of this report, Ritchie called upon General B. F. Tracy, secretary of the United States navy, who did not fail to grasp its significance. Ritchie was leaving shortly for a tour of European metal centres to conduct a campaign for the greater use of nickel, and General Tracy asked if a representative of his department could accompany him. Ritchie was pleased to have this evidence of interest in such a quarter, and General Tracy nominated Lieut. H. B. Buckingham, U.S.N., to make the trip.

Ritchie had not neglected to keep the Canadian government informed of his plans, and thereby gained another companion on his tour. Sir John Macdonald, the Prime Minister, instructed Sir Charles Tupper, High Commissioner in London, to add himself to Ritchie's entourage.

The reports which General Tracy received caused him, probably not without promptings from Ritchie, to order a special plate of nickel-steel armour, as well as a plain steel plate, from the famous Creusot works in France, and a steel plate from Cammel & Co., Sheffield, such as was in use on British warships. The three plates were shipped to the proving grounds at Annapolis, Maryland, set up side by side, and fired at with eight-inch guns.

"The victory of the French nickel-steel plate was so complete over both the other French and English plates that the trial and tests were heralded by telegraph and cables all over the civilized world," wrote Ritchie jubilantly.

Sir Charles Tupper's report to Sir John Macdonald gives some idea of the change in attitude which was then occurring with respect to the importance of Sudbury nickel. Sir Charles wrote in part:

> The best evidence I could obtain of the real importance of the Sudbury mines is the manifest desire both in England and upon the Continent of the largest smelters and consumers of both copper and nickel to become owners of the mines or to control their output.

Ritchie's resisting the temptation to surrender control of his company, its mines or their product, is often cited as evidence of his patriotic desire to retain them for the benefit of Canada and the British Empire; but Ritchie and his associates knew a good thing when they saw it. After pioneering the development of what now seemed sure to become an important and profitable industry, they quite naturally preferred to reap the benefit of their own perseverance.

But credit must be given where credit is due. While Ritchie and the Canadian Copper Company had a monopoly, it was not because of any special privileges accorded them. What they had others could also have. There was still plenty of ground whose owners were only too anxious to sell or enter into any suitable arrangement for development. In fact, several other companies did undertake to open up mines and begin the smelting of ore, with apparently as good a chance as the Canadian Copper Company, but all failed.

The most spectacular, and for Sudbury people the most tragic, was the case of the Vivians. H. H. Vivian & Co., of Swansea, Wales, had a world-wide reputation as smelters and dealers in metals. So successful were they, in fact, that the head of the firm was honoured by the Queen and elevated to the peerage as Lord Swansea.

In 1889, the Vivians bought the Murray property, the first located after ore was exposed by C.P.R. construction crews. Work was immediately begun on buildings and plant, in opening up the deposit, and in erecting a smelter, blown in the following year. Matte, bessemerized at the mine, was shipped to Wales for refining. The difficulty, apparently, was not with the mine, where the ore was of more than average richness (containing about two and one-half per cent nickel), but in the smelting operations. The equipment was not of the best and could turn out only about one-third as much as Dr. Peters was currently producing at Copper Cliff. The English directors made the mistake of thinking they could run a mine by remote control, with the inevitable result. When the mine was finally closed down in 1894, the Vivians were said to have paid $375,000 for their experience.

They were not the only ones to meet defeat in attempting to make nickel mines pay. The Dominion Mineral Company's experience parallels that of the Vivians, beginning in 1889 and ending in 1894. This time there was no question of remote control. The Dominion Mineral Company was composed of Canadian capitalists, including James Worthington, who had built a section of the C.P.R. The company acquired two mineral deposits, the Worthington, west of Sudbury on the Soo line, and the Blezard, northeast of the town. Mining was begun at the latter in 1889, and at the Worthington the following year. A smelter was built at the Blezard, which produced a standard matte containing from eighteen to twenty per cent copper and from twenty-four to twenty-six per cent nickel. In 1893 the Blezard mine was shut down, but the smelter continued for another two years on ore shipped from the Worthington. Failure of the Dominion Mineral Company was attributed to bad management, which seems the most likely explanation.

The year 1889 was prolific in nickel ventures. A company promoted by James Patterson, of Hamilton, Ontario, including a number of the leading business men of that city, was incorporated to operate a nickel refinery in Hamilton based on an electrolytic process patented by Carl Hoepfner. A second company, comprising approximately the same group, was incorporated to operate mines in the Sudbury district to supply matte for the refinery. The Whistle mine in the north-eastern angle of the Basin was bought, and preliminary work begun. One organization controlling all operations from mine to refinery was a sound idea, but unfortunately the Hoepfner process, upon which the scheme depended, did not work.

In 1891, the Drury Nickel Company, operating a prospect in Drury township, about five miles north of

Worthington station, secured its ore from open pits and from a shallow shaft sunk at the bottom of one of the pits. A roast yard was laid out and permanent buildings erected. A smelter of the usual water-jacket type was installed, capable of treating about sixty tons in twenty-four hours. The matte, consigned to the Emmens Company near New York, was transported to Worthington station by an overhead tramway, but the refiners got into financial difficulties, causing the Drury Nickel Company to cease operations. Joseph Wharton of Camden then advanced some money, and the company was re-organized as the Trill Mining and Manufacturing Co., securing an option on a new property in Trill township; but it does not seem to have been any more successful in its second incarnation than in its first.

In 1899, the Great Lakes Copper Company entered the field, purchasing the Mount Nickel property in Blezard township and a prospect in Trill. The Mount Nickel deposit was mined first by means of two pits and a shaft which eventually reached a depth of 165 feet. Mining operations seem to have been efficiently managed, but the smelting works, based on designs of Anton Graf of Vienna, by which high grade matte was to be produced at one operation from green ores, was the weak spot, and when the Graf process failed, the company folded up.

Another combined operations project was that of the Lake Superior Power Company, promoted by F. H. Clergue of Sault Ste. Marie. Desiring to manufacture sulphite pulp, for which sulphur is needed, and also desiring a source of ferro-nickel for treatment in his mills at the Soo, Clergue bought a prospect in Creighton township, which he called the Gertrude, and another in McKim, which he called the Elsie. Development was hindered at first by lack of transportation, but in the spring of 1901 the Manitoulin and North Shore Railway, later called the Algoma Eastern (also owned by Clergue interests) reached the Gertrude mine, and operations began in earnest. Roast yards were prepared and a smelter was blown in in June, 1902, producing from 100 to 160 tons of matte a day. A financial panic in 1903 deprived Clergue of expected American money; the Ontario government came to his support with a $2,000,000 guarantee, but in the reorganization the nickel mines were permanently closed down.

Difficulty in finding a market was the cause of failure in more than one of the above cases, but failure could also be attributed to lack of experience in a highly technical field in which more still remained to be learned than was yet known. How much the success of the Canadian Copper Company, in its later stages, was due to Samuel Ritchie is not apparent, but undoubtedly in its early days, when perseverance and energy were needed, he was there to supply the need.

Ritchie had capable assistants who, by trial and error, were attempting to elucidate the mysteries of nickel metallurgy.

Mining and smelting at Copper Cliff [writes Browne], in the early days was an interesting process, because the methods had to be developed in the face of numerous difficulties. The Canadian Copper Company in 1890 engaged Mr. Jules Garnier to direct their metallurgical progress. Dr. Peters, who had started the smelters in 1888 had by this time gone back to a chicken farm, which then claimed his interest. Mr. Evans, the General Manager, a brilliant civil engineer, and one of the finest amateur entomologists in Canada, filled his days with business and his night with bugs. In this he shone pre-eminent. His office was lined with cigar boxes in which impaled on silver pins and decorated with horrendous nomenclature, thousands of hapless moths and beetles were embalmed. Some such hobby was necessary to keep men from mental stagnation. "I wish," writes the Manager in 1890, "I wish the Dominion Government would establish a line of bull teams so that we can have a regular mail between this and the States. It is sixty hours since we had a mail and it would have been eighty if we had not sent for it!" McArthur of the varied experiences was in charge of the smelter. This contained in 1890 two furnaces, each about 125 tons of ore a day, a marvelous thing to which visitors came and gazed appalled at such a capacity. The matte carrying about 40% copper-nickel piled up high in the yard, much higher than the Company's credit at the bank.

As an authority on the properties and uses of nickel, M. Garnier was unimpeachable, but as an engineer he left much to be desired.

His first work was the erection of a Bessemer plant at Copper Cliff [Browne continues]. The matte which was made in the furnaces was at that time poured out in beds on the yard, and loaded when cold into flat cars. A trestle was built to approach the Bessemer plant. The loaded cars were taken back by a locomotive, run up over a trestle half a mile long into the Bessemer building and there unloaded from the cars onto the ground at exactly the same level as the yard they came from. The matte was then loaded into small hand cars, taken up on an elevator and run out on a circular track which surrounded the remelting furnace.

This remelting furnace was a quaint device. It was a circular brick-lined stack about three feet in diameter with a spiral row of tuyeres [vents for forcing in air] which corkscrewed around it from top to bottom. Outside a spray of water played on the iron shell to keep it cool. Into this matte was charged with quartz and coke for remelting. It does not seem to have occurred to M. Garnier that this remelting of material that was originally in a molten condition was a waste of time and money. . . .

The matte from this furnace was tapped into a spout which conducted it to the Bessemer converters. These Bessemer converters were three and one-half feet in diameter and as originally about eleven feet high. They turned on trunions but were so tall that when turned down they laid their heads on the floor like sick giraffes. McArthur chopped off about two feet of their height so that they could be poured into moulds. . . .

By gradual additions the collection of furnaces at Copper Cliff spread over an ever-widening area,

furnaces being stuck in here and there [says Browne] wherever the ground permitted and whenever the demand warranted it. They were all Herreshoff furnaces fed by what we called the "patent English wheel barrow system." There were no labour-saving devices, the methods employed were crude. The Copper Cliff, Stobie and Evans mines supplied all the ore from 1888 till 1898, when No. 1 and No. 2 mines were started. At that time these were called the McArthur and Great Jones mines. . . .

The ore was all roasted by contract. First at 20 cents a ton, and in 1893 at 17 cents a ton. This work was done by Dan McKinnon and his contract called for roast ore to contain not over 7% sulphur. The piles were very large and high and were burned for about six months. The pile of Stobie ore I timed and found it ceased to smoke nine months after it was fired.

From the start of the nickel industry there had been a demand for the refining of nickel in Canada, instead of in Europe or the United States. When, in 1886, the Canadian Copper Company was applying to parliament for authority to operate in Canada, it had requested "power to sell and treat its ores in such part or parts of Canada or elsewhere" as it should deem proper, but the words *or elsewhere* had been deleted by the Private Bills Committee, and Mr. Ritchie, who was present, "agreed on the part of the company that the company should do its refining in Canada." This undertaking had never been fulfilled.

Following the imposition in 1897 by the Ontario government of regulations requiring the manufacture in Canada of sawlogs cut on Crown lands, the agitation for an export duty on nickel and copper was greatly increased. Newspapers all over Canada took sides, and boards of trade passed resolutions. The Council of the Toronto Board of Trade adopted a resolution in favour of a duty. In Sudbury opinions differed, and Frank Cochrane, mayor that year, was censured by some for having wired the Toronto Board of Trade in opposition to the duty.

The most important event in the history of Sudbury subsequent to the incorporation of the Canadian Copper Company was the decision, in 1898, of Dr. Ludwig Mond to buy nickel properties in the district to provide matte for the refinery he proposed building in Wales. Mond went about the matter methodically. Before arriving at a decision he sent two emissaries, Carl Langer and Bernard Mohr, to investigate and report upon the possibility of acquiring suitable mines.

The report was favourable, and Dr. Mond invited Rinaldo McConnell to go to London to discuss the purchase of property. McConnell arrived in January, 1899, to find that Mond was in Italy. Following him there, McConnell offered to sell his property in Denison township, generally called the McConnell mine, and also his seven-eighths interest in the Cryderman mine, later called the Garson. Mond bought outright McConnell's share of the Garson for $30,000, and undertook to buy the property in Denison for $200,000 if, after five months' test, 200,000 tons of ore "with at least five per cent of nickel plus copper" could be shown, the cost of the test to be advanced by Mond but to be deducted from the purchase price in case of a sale.

McConnell's exploratory work satisfied Mond concerning the Denison property, and McConnell returned to London to close the deal and discuss further plans, including the building of a smelter near the Victoria mine, as it was renamed. The Canadian Copper Company was induced to sell its one-eighth interest in the Garson mine, and within the year Mond had invested $320,000 in his Sudbury properties. In 1900 the Mond Nickel Company Limited was incorporated. These were encouraging signs to the many prospectors and others holding properties in the hope of either a sale or money for development.

In 1901 the eminent inventor, Thomas A. Edison, became interested in the mining possibilities of Sudbury. After visiting the Pan-American Exhibition at Buffalo, where he had seen samples of Sudbury ore in an exhibit of the Ontario Bureau of Mines, Edison had come to Sudbury to see if he might find nickel and cobalt for use in his electrical equipment.

With Mr. Edison and his wife were Mrs. Edison's brother, J. V. Miller, and two others. The Edison party were besieged by prospectors with mining claims to sell, and Mr. Edison expressed surprise that no one in Canada seemed prepared to spend money in developing mines, all seemed anxious to sell. He failed to realize how scarce money was in Canada at that time for such ventures as mining.

Mr. Edison opened an office in Sudbury and he and his associates spent several weeks examining properties in various parts of the district, chiefly in the eastern part, where they conducted a dip-needle survey. Following this, properties were secured in Falconbridge township, and the sinking of a shaft was begun. The overburden was heavy; the shaft encountered quicksands a short distance above bedrock, and was discontinued. This ended Edison's mining activities in the Sudbury district, but later drilling proved that if his shaft had been continued down into the rock it would have found ore.

# VII

# *"Old Nick" Gives Trouble*

ALTHOUGH NOT RECOGNIZED AS AN element until 1751, nickel as an alloy had been in use since the first armourers had begun to hammer swords out of metal. One of these early artisans discovered that sword blades made from meteorites could surpass in keenness those made from any other metal, not knowing that meteoric iron was usually combined with another metal, giving it exceptional hardness.

In very early times, the Chinese had learned to make beautiful objects from a white metal produced by adding zinc to copper-nickel ores, although at that time they were ignorant of the existence of nickel. This alloy the Chinese called "paktong," and during the seventeenth century articles made of it were imported into Europe by the East India Company.

In the meantime, miners in Saxony had discovered copper ores which they attempted to smelt by processes already familiar, but the result was not the usual red metal, but a lighter, very hard one, so hard that they could do nothing with it. In an age of superstition, it was perhaps natural that the miners should have believed their copper ore was bewitched, and they called it "kupfer-nickel," or "Old Nick's copper."

Scientists, however, were not inclined to such superstitious beliefs. A Swedish scientist named Cronstedt, after five years' experimentation, isolated the new element;

and in memory of the Saxon miners he called it nickel.
Five years later another Swedish scientist, Von Engestrom,
analyzed paktong and proved it to be an alloy of copper,
nickel and zinc.    This laid the basis of a new industry for
European metal workers, the paktong of the Chinese
becoming German, or nickel, silver.

Such uses, however, did not provide a very large market
for the refractory metal, and existing sources were able to
supply the need.    The next step came with the introduction
of electro-plating in 1844.    This made possible the silver-
plating of German silver articles, and German silver
continues to be the basis of most silver plate.

Nickel for coins followed.    The first coin containing
nickel was authorized by the United States government in
1857, a one-cent piece containing twelve per cent nickel.
This was soon discontinued, but in 1866 the United States
began minting a five-cent coin containing twenty-five per
cent nickel and seventy-five per cent copper, an alloy which
has become standard for coins that are not pure nickel.
Belgium, in 1861, had adopted four nickel-copper coins of
various denominations; Switzerland adopted the first pure
nickel coin in 1887.    Up to the outbreak of World War I,
nickel coins of varying denominations had been adopted
by fifty-four countries, but Canada, the chief producer of
nickel, did not have a coin containing nickel until 1922.

The first nickel mines began producing in Norway in
1840; but after 1877 the French island of New Caledonia
in the South Seas became the world's chief source of nickel,
and held that honour till it was supplanted by Sudbury
mines in the early years of the twentieth century.

As has been said, the prospectors who staked the mines,
and even Ritchie himself, did not suspect that the ore
contained nickel.    Ritchie first learned of it when he
received a complaint from Col. Thompson of the Orford
Copper Company that ore shipped by the Canadian Copper
Company contained only four and one-half per cent of
copper instead of the seven per cent specified (specially
picked ore).

"Ritchie came on to New York in a towering rage," wrote the Colonel, "and asserted that we were trying to swindle him. 'Ritchie,' said I, 'you have never taken the trouble to have a complete analysis made of your ore. There is only four and one-half per cent copper, but there is also two and one-half per cent nickel.'"[1]

That was a poser for Ritchie, but it was also a challenge for Thompson, and he decided to tackle the problem of evolving a process for the extraction of nickel from Sudbury ore. Making sudden decisions was not a new thing with him.

Colonel (an honorary title) Robert M. Thompson had graduated from the United States naval academy, but after a few years at sea had resigned from the navy to study law at Harvard, and upon graduation had opened a law office in Boston. Among his clients was a Boston capitalist, W. E. C. Eustis, who had organized the Orford Nickel Company to develop a nickel mine near Orford, Quebec. Because of the refractory nature of the ore the company had looked about for a copper sulphide property to provide a suitable fluxing ore and had located one near Capleton, Quebec. Its owners were in England, and Eustis sent Thompson there to negotiate a lease. Thompson came to the conclusion that it would be cheaper to buy the property, which he proceeded to do without consulting his client. Eustis, however, went along with Thompson in the matter; the company was reorganized and Thompson became general manager.

Thompson, like the mountain climber who is always intent on some higher peak ahead, now got the idea of a smelter at a convenient spot on tidewater. With this end in view he bought four acres of submerged land along the New Jersey shore, and persuaded New York city officials to dump ashes and other refuse upon the property. In time the waters receded, the land appeared above the level of the tides, and the Orford Copper Company had a valuable smelter site.

[1] Quoted by D. H. Browne.

With a smelter so advantageously located, Thompson soon had so much ore coming to him that he found it more profitable to continue custom smelting than to attempt to smelt ore from Quebec; and consequently shipping from Capleton was discontinued. In this way Thompson became acquainted with the Montana magnate, W. A. Clark, from whom he secured the money to buy out his Boston associates, reorganizing the company as the Orford Copper Company.

Thompson now seemed well established in the business of smelting copper, and had apparently divested himself of all connection with nickel. Yet it was as a nickel metallurgist and one of the founders of the greatest nickel corporation in the world that he was to become internationally known.

Although the Orford Copper Company could doubtless have done well as a smelter of copper, in which it was now well established, Thompson saw in the Sudbury nickel ore another peak ahead; and it was not in his nature to refuse a challenge. Little was yet known about the metallurgy of nickel, and what was known was a private matter. In Wales, H. H. Vivian & Co. were producing nickel, but their process was their own affair. The New Caledonia Nickel Company, with headquarters in Paris, was producing most of the world's nickel, but it also kept its methods secret; furthermore, its ore differed from that at Sudbury. Joseph Wharton, in Camden, also produced nickel, but by almost laboratory methods. Nickel was selling at $1 a pound, and world production in 1886 was less than 1,000 tons.

The chief method of reducing nickel ores was by wet processes. Matte was ground up and treated with sulphuric acid, dissolving the nickel and iron, setting free sulphuretted hydrogen which precipitated the copper. The solution of nickel and iron sulphate was then crystallized and roasted, forming a red oxide of nickel and iron. The residue contained so much copper sulphide, however, that the action of the acid was very slow, and the slimy mass required remelting in order to oxidize the sulphur.

Obviously, this process would need to be improved if nickel was to be produced commercially at a price admitting of wider use. The Colonel doggedly continued his experiments.

One day [he wrote], I was wandering idly through the smelter yard with a hammer in my hand. The matte, which was made by re-smelting the residues from our acid treatment was piled in the yard in cones as it was dumped from the little matte pots. One of these cones did not look the same as the others. I tapped it with my hammer and to my surprise it fell into two pieces. The top was dull and dark, the bottom was shiny and yellow. I called the furnace foreman and asked for an explanation. No explanation was forthcoming. Finally the yard sweeper confessed that he had the day before cleaned out the chemical house and having a wheel barrow of such cleanings that he did not know what to do with, he had dumped it into the matte furnace. Charles Bartlett, the foreman, and I began a systematic search for the reason. We found that the bottom of the pot had a great deal more nickel than copper, while the top carried more copper than nickel. We commenced to experiment, melting in crucibles some matte with every chemical we had in the warehouse. For a long time we had no results, finally when we used soda carbonate we got a reaction. The separation was very imperfect and we had to remelt the bottom part many times before we obtained a fairly good nickel sulphide.

I went to Philadelphia, shut myself up for a week and tried to work out the chemistry of it. I knew very little about the subject but I applied for a patent. In due time I was notified that a patent had been taken out in 1877 by Wm. B. Tatro, a shoe maker of Hartford, Connecticut and Tatro had experimented on a kitchen stove, melting various chemicals with the ore. He had patented a mixture of lime, fluorspar, saltpetre, salt and potash which when melted with the ore formed an alkaline sulphide, and this caused the same separation as the soda sulphide I had used. Vivian of Wales was using what they called "Sally Nixon," which is sulphate of soda, the old Sal Enixum, or washed out salt, which is left in making hydrochloric acid from common salt, but I knew nothing of this at the time.

I went down to Connecticut and found that Tatro had died several years ago and that his patents had been transferred to a small company, nearly every stockholder of which had died. I applied for administration papers and had the company brought back to life. I purchased Tatro's patent from them. To his ideas and to my own, many improvements suggested by experience were afterwards added.[1]

Thus was discovered the Orford process of refining nickel, sometimes called the "tops and bottoms process," which for many years was to be one of the principal methods in use. It finally gave way to electrolytic refining.

While Thompson was wrestling with his problem in New Jersey, Dr. Carl Langer, an Austrian chemical engineer in the employ of Alfred Mond, a manufacturing chemist in England, was also working on a process for the extraction of nickel from nickel-copper ores.

The process as finally evolved consisted of first extracting copper from matte with sulphuric acid and crystallizing the solution to form copper sulphate, then reducing the residue to a finely divided metallic powder and treating it with carbon monoxide gas. This picked up the nickel, forming what was called nickel carbonyl. On passing this gas over heated nickel shot the gas was decomposed and each grain of shot received a coating of nickel. The shot then proceeded back and forth through the apparatus, receiving coat after coat of nickel until, having reached a certain size, it was eliminated by a screen.

Ludwig Mond, the prime mover in this enterprise, was of German origin. He had settled in England some twenty years previously and had established a prosperous chemical manufacturing business in Cheshire. As an aid to his business he had set up an experimental laboratory in London, and it was in this laboratory that Carl Langer worked.

The discovery of a nickel refining process was more or less an accident. Mond at the time was interested in perfecting a process for the production of bleaching powder as a by-product of what was known as the "ammonia-soda" process. In this, it was necessary to vaporize ammonium chloride; because of the corrosive effect of ammonium

[1]Quoted by D. H. Browne.

chloride on most metals, iron tanks lined with glazed tile were adopted; and as nickel did not seem to be affected by the vapour, the tank valves were made of pure nickel.

The scheme worked perfectly in the laboratory, but when a large-scale plant was built it was found that the valves became so encrusted with carbon that they would not work properly. It was then discovered that whereas in the laboratory a current of pure carbon dioxide was used to clear the apparatus of ammonia, in the larger plant the carbon dioxide contained a small percentage of carbon monoxide. Thus the latter's affinity for nickel became known.

Once this was understood the discovery of a process for refining nickel inevitably followed; but this involved a great deal of additional time and effort. In 1892, after securing a patent, Mond built an experimental plant at Smethwick, near Birmingham, on land belonging to Henry Wiggin & Co., refiners of nickel by processes already in use.

As eventually worked out, the Mond process comprised five operations: (1) roasting matte to drive out as much of the sulphur as possible; (2) extracting about two-thirds of the copper by sulphuric acid, the resulting sulphate of copper being sold in that form; (3) reducing the nickel and remaining copper to a metallic state by water gas rich in hydrogen, with the temperature, never over 400°C., under perfect control; (4) taking the residue through air-tight conveyors and elevators into the "volatizer," where it was subjected to the action of carbon monoxide gas at a temperature not exceeding 80°C.; and (5) passing the nickel carbonyl thus produced into a "decomposer," a tower or horizontal retort heated to 180°C., where the nickel was released in a metallic state.

The operation was not completed in one passage through the five stages. The materials were made to circulate between stages three and four for a period varying from seven to fifteen days, until about sixty per cent of the nickel had been removed as carbonyl. The residue was returned to the first operation and followed the same course as before. When complete, the product contained between ninety-nine and four-tenths and ninety-nine and eight-tenths per cent nickel.

At first, Mond had no intention of going into nickel production, and tried to sell his process. For about two years the Canadian Copper Company considered it, but lost interest as the Orford process became more successful. Not the least of the reasons for the Canadian Copper Company's decision was the need for such extreme care in operating the process. Since the gas was very poisonous, constant vigilance was required to detect leaks. Effects of the gas were not noticeable; workmen who had gradually received a poisonous dose would go to bed apparently well; but, as one of their companions is reported to have said, "when they woke up they were dead."

Mond eventually eliminated most of the operational difficulties and, having failed to sell, proceeded with plans for a refinery at Clydach, Wales, and looked about for a source of nickel ore, which took him to Sudbury and the establishing of a very prosperous enterprise.

While Thompson and Langer were attempting to solve the problem of refining nickel, a Swedish metallurgist, Noak Victor Hybinette, had solved it by developing an electrolytic process which was to be the forerunner of processes now generally in use. He had been in charge of a refinery in Norway producing nickel for sale at sixty cents a pound when word came that the Orford Copper Company had agreed to supply nickel to the United States government for thirty cents a pound. This caused the Norwegian plant to close down.

It also caused Hybinette to emigrate to the United States, where he found employment with the Orford Copper Company itself and later with the International Nickel Company. He tried to interest both in his refining process, but was unsuccessful. Although a capable metallurgist and scientist, he lacked the faculty of getting along with people.

Returning to Norway, he built a refinery at Kristiansand in 1910 to treat ore from mines recently opened in that country.  Several times enlarged, the plant in 1914 was capable of producing annually 1,800 tons of nickel and 1,200 tons of copper.

It is of interest that the refinery manager was Anton Gronningsater who had already spent a number of years in the Sudbury field and was to spend the greater part of his subsequent life in association with its mines.  Born near Aalesund, Norway, in 1880, a graduate in chemical engineering of the Trondheim Technological Institute, with postgraduate study in metallurgy at Freiberg, Germany, he, too, had gone to the United States and had got a job with International Nickel, first at Constable Hook, N.J., and later at Copper Cliff, where he became chief chemist in charge of the plant producing cobalt oxide.  Leaving Inco to take a position with the Deloro Mining and Reduction Company, which he held for two years, he returned to Kristiansand to become manager of the refinery, remaining there for almost ten years.

# VIII

# *Town of Sudbury*

BY IMPERCEPTIBLE DEGREES THE UN-
planned frontier community became a
town, although still technically a village and part of
McKim township. By the early nineties it was evident
to the far-seeing that, despite metallurgical and other
problems yet to be solved, the nickel industry held great
possibilities. The lumber trade was still important, but it
could be only a temporary influence; Sudbury's fate was
linked to nickel.

A sign of the growing feeling of permanence among the
citizens was the number of flourishing fraternal and mutual
benefit societies. Within the first few years of the community's existence, the I.O.O.F., A.O.U.W., C.M.B.A.,
R.T. of T., Sons of Scotland, and Masonic and Orange
lodges were organized. They were handicapped at first by
lack of suitable lodge rooms; but as more permanent
buildings appeared this need was better supplied.

Further evidence of permanence was to be seen in the
type of business premises that had succeeded the first rude
shacks. All, of course, were built of wood; brick buildings
had not yet made their appearance. While the corner of
Durham and Elm was generally considered to be the hub of
the business district, Larch Street west of Durham for a
time vied with it in importance.

Before Sudbury emerged, the Hudson's Bay Company
had had a trading post on Whitefish Lake, a few miles to

73

the southwest; but when the Indians began by-passing the post for the bright lights of Sudbury, the company built a store on Larch Street, and brought T. B. Ross from Whitefish Lake to take charge of it. After the company finally pulled out in 1897, the premises were occupied by Purvis Brothers, hardware merchants. On the east, at the corner of Larch and Durham, was Robert Martin's shoe store, while near the corner of Larch and Elgin was the Russell Hotel.

Those were the days when a dollar was a lot of money. With a dollar, the thrifty housewife could buy a ten-pound mutton roast, or a twelve-and-one-half-pound roast of beef. If she were content with beef stew, she could get it for five cents a pound. A. Paul offered Victoria cloth at nine cents, flannelette at eight cents, and grey wool flannel at twenty, twenty-two and twenty-five cents a yard.

Sudbury merchants knew nothing of the more beguiling type of advertising that was being evolved by the metro-politan stores; they believed in letting price do the talking. But the Hudson's Bay Company seems to have established some sort of record when it offered "blankets, from $6.50 to $10.00; good blankets from $3.00 to $5.50; and *poor* blankets from $2.00 to $2.50."

That Sudbury had become a place of some importance was demonstrated when, on March 5, 1891, the first issue of the Sudbury *Journal* made its appearance. It was an eight-page, five-column paper, four pages of which were devoted to news of Sudbury and surrounding settlements and advertisements of local merchants and professional men (and one woman). The other four pages consisted of "boiler plate." Papers of this sort were common at the time—and can still be found. They were produced by publishers who supplied them already printed on one side, the other left blank for the use of the local newspaper man. The "boiler plate" pages contained very lurid or highly romantic serial stories, items of world news, poetry, jokes, anecdotes about famous people, recipes, national advertising (chiefly devoted to patent medicines) and other items considered to be of general interest. For example, Vol. 1, No. 1 of the *Journal* contained an instalment of a serial entitled "A Barytone's Devotion, or a Tale of Sunny Italy," and among the items of world news were those headed: SOMEONE CRIED "FIRE"; A RAILWAY HORROR; and A BARONESS MURDERED.

The *Journal* declared that it was "devoted to the mining interests and development of Nipissing and Algoma districts," and claimed to be "the only paper printed in Sudbury, or within a radius of 79 miles east on the C.P.R. to North Bay; 133 miles southwest on the Soo R.R. to Thessalon; and 550 miles west to Port Arthur." The paper was produced by the Journal Printing and Publishing Company; J. A. Orr, Manager.

With the advent of the *Journal* Sudbury not only gained a newspaper which was to help greatly in developing community spirit, and was to put the place on the map in so far as the outside world was concerned, but it acquired in "Jimmy" Orr a citizen who for the rest of his long life was to make the interests of Sudbury his own. He was typical of the best of the printer-editors much more common then than now. First and foremost, he was a capable printer, as the typographical excellence of his paper amply attests. In addition, he wrote well, if perhaps somewhat addicted to an over-profuse style: he never let one word suffice if two could be employed. This was all the more strange in that everything had to be set by hand. Jimmy did most of his "writing" at the case. During its earlier years, Jimmy produced most of the copy, attended ball games, council meetings, and other public events, and wrote the editorials. His style, while not markedly peculiar, was sufficiently individual to be recognized in whatever he contributed to the paper.

An editorial in the *Journal's* first issue fairly well sums up the feelings of the people it hoped to serve:

The Sudbury *Journal* comes before you a candidate for your favour. That favour it will try to win by a career of usefulness. Our first effort will be to give all the news that is worth giving about Sudbury and the marvellous district of which it is the commercial centre; our next to maintain and defend the rights and interests of the people of this district.

We recognize the fact at the outset that Sudbury is unique, that there is no other place like it in the world. We have here the bull's eye of a great new district of Canadian territory, a district for long neglected because of its supposed poverty, but now the centre of potential wealth. Nickel, one of the precious metals, hitherto drawn in small quantities by mere laboratory processes from refractory ores is found here in masses, whose value none can state, because the most conservative estimate looks like wild exaggeration. Though not yet an incorporated village, Sudbury has already attracted greater attention and is more widely known than almost any other place in Canada, outside of our larger cities. It is the meeting place of two great railway lines, and the objective point of others that are to be built within a short time. It may be predicted with reasonable certainty that Sudbury, as the centre of the greatest nickel district in the world, has a splendid future before it. It shall be our aim to be worthy of the place we represent. This is a high and honourable ambition, and we ask of the public such help as the *Journal* shall prove worthy of, and such consideration as may fairly be claimed by those who honestly try to live up to good professions.

The advent of a newspaper was a boon to those who from time to time found it imperative to give expression to their views and opinions. Two of these were Æneas McCharles and James Stobie, well-known prospectors, who had been conducting a campaign against proposed amendments to the mining laws. In the issue of June 18, 1891, however, Stobie had a long letter in which he advocated secession from Ontario of the districts of Nipissing and Algoma and the creation of a new province. This was not the last proposal that would be made in that direction.

The *Journal* was to continue for twenty-seven years, until in the middle of the year 1918 it would run down like an unwound clock. It can be said that, except for a few final years when it showed evidence of decline, no paper ever served its community as faithfully and unselfishly as the *Journal* did the Sudbury district.

With a newspaper having such an exalted opinion of Sudbury and its future, in which the citizens doubtless joined, it was perhaps natural that there should have developed a desire for a more exalted status than that of an unincorporated village, and from time to time there had been talk of the advantages to be gained by incorporation as a town. Finally, the *Journal* of January 14, 1892 (and subsequent issues) contained the following:

### NOTICE

Of Application for Incorporation of the TOWN OF SUDBURY

Application will be made to the Legislative Assembly of the Province of Ontario, at the next session thereof, for an Act to incorporate a certain portion of the Township of McKim, known as the Village of Sudbury, in the said Township of McKim, as the Town of Sudbury.

Dated this 14th day of January, A.D., 1892.

(Sgd) William R. White
*Solicitor for Applicant.*

A week later a public meeting was held with Reeve Fournier in the chair and Township Clerk Ryan as secretary to discuss details of the proposed incorporation. A committee was appointed to determine the amount of assessable property within the limits of the proposed town and the income that could be expected.

Although there seemed to be general agreement as to the desirability of incorporation, there were undercurrents of dissatisfaction with the manner in which township affairs were being conducted, and there was a desire, at least on the part of some citizens, for a change. This feeling was brought into the open on February 20th, when an official protest was lodged by Gus Harwood, defeated candidate for Reeve, against the election of the entire council, charging bribery, illegality, hiring of teams, and other irregularities. The protest was the talk of the countryside and everyone awaited developments with varying interest, depending on individual sympathy. Those interested were to have a

long wait and to experience something of the law's delays
before a decision was reached.

An inkling of the cross-currents agitating the village
may be gained from the following item which appeared in
the *Journal* of March 3rd.

### THE TOWN OF SUDBURY

The gentlemen who have been promoting the incorporation of
the town to suit their own particular views in their own way,
have not been altogether successful.   In the Bill of incorporation
the town was divided as follows: "Ryan Ward" was composed
of all that part of the town lying east of a straight line drawn
through the centre of Lisgar Street, from north to south. "Fournier Ward" comprised all that portion lying between the westerly
limit of Ryan Ward and a straight line running through the centre
of Elgin Street from north to south; and "McCormick Ward"
was composed of all that portion lying west of the westerly limit
of Fournier Ward.

As those opposed to this division of the Wards, and also to
the names given them, were allowed to have no say in the matter,
a largely-signed petition was secured, and a map of the town
and proposed wards prepared and forwarded to the legislature.
The matter came up before the Private Bills Committee of the
House on Tuesday, and the opposition representatives, Messrs.
A. Paul and Dr. Struthers, had no difficulty in convincing the
members that their plan was the fairest and most equitable of the
two, and decided so by a vote of 12 to 5.

As amended by the Committee the wards are as follows:
"West Ward" is the same as proposed in the Bill as McCormick
Ward, namely all west of Elgin Street; "North Ward" is composed of all that portion of the town lying east of Elgin Street
and north of Elm Street; and "South Ward" of that portion
lying east of Elgin Street and south of Elm Street.   This division
is a much fairer one as regards the number of voters in each ward,
as the proposed Fournier Ward would have contained more than
both the others.   The Committee also struck out the clause
providing for the election of a Reeve, as there is no likelihood of a
County Council in this part of the country for many years.   The
Council of the town will be composed of a Mayor, and three
Councillors from each of the three wards.

The objectors did not have it all their own way, however,
for in the *Journal* of April 7th, a report of the third reading
of the Sudbury Bill stated that the promoters had suc-

ceeded in having the Legislature override the Private Bills Committee to the extent that the names of the wards were changed back to those originally suggested; the division of the town proposed by the objectors was accepted, but West Ward was to be called Ryan instead of McCormick, while the North Ward would be known as Fournier, and South Ward, McCormick.

Andrew McNaughton's death had left the town without a Magistrate. The vacancy was filled in June by the temporary appointment of W. A. Quibell, of Sault Ste. Marie, who was to continue in the position for many years and to become one of Sudbury's leading citizens.

Early in June, a fire had destroyed the court house and gaol as well as the residence of the gaoler. The government took immediate steps to rebuild, and by fall a new brick building, thirty-four by sixty-five feet, with stone foundation, two storeys high, had been built. It contained, in addition to thirteen cells and quarters for the gaoler, the court room, judge's room and jury room.

Meanwhile, the protest against the election of the sitting Council was wending its way through the courts, those on either side being apparently about evenly matched when it came to motions and counter motions; but eventually, on October 19, 1892, the Master in Chambers at Osgoode Hall, to whom the matter had been referred by the Chief Justice of the Common Pleas Division, rendered a lengthy and elaborate judgment dealing with the points raised by the Relator, Mr. Harwood, in the notice of motion, which were:

1. The Clerk of the Township did not act as the Returning Officer, and the election was not conducted by the proper officer.

2. There was no defaulters' list used by the Returning Officer.

3. Income voters were allowed to vote at the election without showing that their taxes were paid.

4. There was no certificate in the hands of the Returning Officer showing the date when the assessment roll was returned to the Clerk, and when finally revised by the Stipendiary Magistrate.

5. The Returning Officer used the wrong date in the oath administered to the voters.

6. The refusal of the Returning Officer to administer the oath to a voter, although requested to do so by the agent of the Relator.

7. The inability of a large number of voters to vote owing to the want of an additional polling booth.

8. Bribery by the Respondents Anctil and Fournier.

The Master held the first seven objections to be good, especially the seventh, which by itself would have been enough to void the election. With respect to the eighth objection, he held that Councillor Anctil was guilty of personal bribery, but gave the benefit of the doubt to Reeve Fournier. The Master therefore unseated the whole Council. An appeal was taken against this ruling, but it was lost, and the Council, after having sat through nearly the whole year, was finally unseated on November 11th. Consequently, the *Journal* of December 1st carried the following advertisement:

### MUNICIPAL ELECTIONS

In the High Court of Justice, Queen's Bench Division

By virtue of a certain order of the Master in Chambers at the City of Toronto, dated 19th day of October, A.D. 1892, notice is hereby given that a meeting of the electors of the Township of McKim will be held in the Town Hall, Sudbury, on

### TUESDAY, DECEMBER 8TH, 1892

at 10 o'clock in the forenoon, for the nomination of candidates for the offices of Reeve and Councillors for the said Township of McKim for the remainder of the present year and that in the event of a poll being required for the above offices, or any of them, the same will be held at the usual places on THURSDAY, 15TH DECEMBER, 1892.

WM. MOFFAT,
*Sheriff, County Renfrew.*

**Dated** at Pembroke this 28th day of November, 1892.

On the appointed day Sheriff Moffat presided at the meeting, prepared to receive nominations. With the exception of Jos. Anctil, convicted of bribery, the old Council was re-elected by acclamation, Stephen Fournier evidently willing to accept the benefit of the doubt. In Anctil's place Louis Laforest was elected.

The Council would continue to act for the balance of the month, after which a new Council would be elected and would represent the township only. Sudbury would be a town after the first of the year and would need to elect a mayor and nine councillors. On December 29th, the ratepayers gathered at McCormick's Hall to nominate their new council, which was elected without a contest.

It consisted of: Mayor, Stephen Fournier; Councillors, Fournier Ward—A. Gallagher, Edmond Migneron, D. A. Rioux; McCormick Ward—A. Paul, R. Martin, Dr. W. H. Mulligan; Ryan Ward—D. O'Connor, Dr. R. B. Struthers, T. M. Kirkwood.

D. L. McKinnon became Reeve of McKim, now shorn of Sudbury.

As Sudbury entered on its first year as an incorporated town, the population, according to assessor George Loney, was close to 1,400, and the assessed value of property on the rolls was $235,000. On April 13, 1893, the *Journal* reported that the town had been crowded with shantymen during the past couple of weeks, and in consequence business had been good with the merchants, and presumably with the saloons. Men were leaving to begin the drive, for which wages of from $2 to $2.75 a day were being offered.

From the start, Sudbury had been noted for its hotels, and as 1893 opened, Mrs. Morton was having the White House thoroughly overhauled and repainted, new carpets laid down and other improvements made. Messrs. Rothschild and Wilson had taken possession of the National Hotel, to which extensive alterations and improvements were being made. Among other things, the bar had been moved to a corner location, and the proprietors claimed that it was the largest and finest in town.    At the Balmoral, Messrs. Perkins and Warren were also making changes. And finally, Messrs. Doyle and Millar had bought the American Hotel, formerly the Revere House, which had apparently failed under the management of S. May.

Three bróthers, immigrants from Poland, Aaron, Meyer and Hiram Silverman, had begun business during the early nineties, peddling from packsacks and eventually opened small stores side by side on Elgin Street.   Hiram soon left Sudbury, but the others remained to add interesting strains to the warp and woof of Sudbury society.   When Aaron died full of years in 1941 his Elm Street department store was the largest in town, with his two sons Saul and Jack already trained in its management, eager to continue the traditions established by their father.   Meyer's son Max, as eminent in his own way as his cousins, has chosen an entirely different way of life as a sports promoter, and is probably best known as the manager of Sudbury's hockey team, the Wolves.

Now that Sudbury had become a town, it was faced with the necessity of correcting many shortcomings which might have been overlooked in a village.   One of the most pressing was the provision of an adequate water supply.   Within a month after its first issue, the *Journal* had drawn attention to this need:

The water supply is another vexed question in Sudbury. The public is at present compelled to draw water from a single spring outside the town, at a spot absolutely unprotected from cattle and dogs, and we have been informed that women some-times go to the small tank there to rinse their clothes in our drinking water!  Again, some cannot afford to have their water drawn from there even, and use water from the creek which is the main sewer of the place.  This should be stopped.  Either arrangements could be made to have pure water piped into the town, or artesian wells bored and good drinking water secured, as determined by careful analysis, and distributed according to need to various points.  This matter should receive early attention.

In the minds of many the need for adequate sewage disposal was linked with a proper water system, and there was much discussion of the problem during 1893. Others went even farther and suggested that the time had come to install a system of electric lighting. At length, on October 25th, a public meeting was held at which the whole matter was discussed. Most of those present were in favour of proceeding at once with waterworks, but there was a division of opinion concerning the advisability of electric lights. The inevitable committee was appointed to secure further information concerning the various proposals.

At the end of its first year as a town, Sudbury's financial statement showed a total revenue of $13,199.02 and expenditures of $12,580.16.

At the end of his first year as Mayor, Stephen Fournier retired, but not permanently, for he would again be Mayor. With Fournier out of the running, the town was stirred with interest as to who his successor would be. Election contests still reflected religious divisions, and the one held on January 1, 1894, was no exception. Dan O'Connor was the Catholic nominee and A. Paul the Protestant. O'Connor was elected by a vote of 113 to 110.

Activity in the mines was at a low point, as it had been during the past three years. New markets had not yet been established for nickel, and the price had dropped to forty-five cents a pound. "Very naturally the few companies operating here now are not over anxious to see others coming in," wrote the Sudbury correspondent of the Montreal *Herald*, "and some of them are more than suspected of using their influence to keep others out. It is said that intending investors, when they come here, are told the present companies are able to supply all the demand. . . ."

On the other hand, a gold mining boom had developed near Lake Wanapitei, and glowing reports were received of the richness of some of the strikes. One quartz ledge three hundred yards long and seventy-five feet wide was reported to contain an average of $8.50 gold and $5.75 silver a ton. There would be other gold prospects in the Wanapitei region, and some rich specimens would be recovered, but no extensive deposits of gold-bearing ore would be found.

Originally the Nipissing electoral district comprised all the territory from the Ottawa River to Thunder Bay and north to James Bay. After the railway went through, Algoma was carved out of the western part, with the dividing line following the western boundary of McKim township. This new district was divided later into East and West ridings. Seat of the judicial district, however, was at Renfrew. In 1894 the provincial government decided to create the judicial district of Nipissing and for some obscure reason left the choice of its seat to be decided by ballot. Mattawa, North Bay and Sturgeon Falls each wanted the honour. The people of Sudbury, realizing that because the town was so near the western boundary of the district they would be out of the running, were mostly in favour of North Bay.

The contest was one which Sudburians could enjoy without any sense of loss. Confident that some day Sudbury itself would be the centre of a new judicial district, they were interested mainly in having the seat near enough for convenience and far enough away so as not to conflict with their own aspirations when the time should come. Mattawa, North Bay and Sturgeon Falls each opened campaign rooms in the opposing towns and in Sudbury, with pluggers and rooters whooping it up for their respective communities. North Bay won, Sudbury voting 92 for Mattawa, 140 for North Bay and 3 for Sturgeon Falls. But North Bay was not to get the plum so easily. A protest was lodged against it on the ground of some alleged skulduggery and the government ordered another contest which North Bay again won. Joseph A. Valin, an Ottawa lawyer, became the first judge of the Judicial District of Nipissing.

Two significant items appeared in the same issue of the *Journal* (March 22, 1894). The first was as follows:

A public meeting was called by the Mayor on Tuesday evening for the purpose of discussing better fire protection for the town. Only six persons were present, so no action was taken.

The other was:

### THE WORST BLAZE YET!
### St. Ann's R.C. Church Destroyed

A small portion of the walls and two corner towers is all that remains standing as we write this (Good Friday) morning of the fine R.C. Church, the principal ornament of our town, from an architectural point of view. . . .

The Church, 150 x 60 feet in size, was commenced six years ago, but not completed. About $13,000 had already been expended upon it. When finished the cost was expected to be at least $20,000. The insurance amounts to $6,000. . . .

In the following issue two items appeared relating to men who were to have an influence in Sudbury affairs. The first was the announcement of the purchase by Frank Cochrane of the property at the corner of Cedar and Durham streets upon which he proposed to erect a three-storey brick building to house his fast-growing business. The other concerned the sale of the jewellery business formerly conducted by A. H. Beath to J. S. Gill, lately arrived from Orillia to make his home in Sudbury. Mr. Beath would re-enter the jewellery business, and the Gill name would attain a prominent place among the citizens of Sudbury.

Meantime the agitation for waterworks, sewage disposal and electric lights had not lagged, and on August 15, 1894, the property owners were asked to vote on by-laws to provide these utilities. The waterworks by-law called for the raising of $30,000 to be repaid over a period of thirty years, and the electric light by-law, with which was linked the sewerage system, called for an expenditure of $10,000. Both were carried by large majorities.

At the end of its first decade Sudbury could point with satisfaction to a record of steady, if at times slow, progress. It had developed from a settlement of shacks into a town showing signs of permanence. During 1894, new building to the value of $55,000 had been undertaken. Of this, Frank Cochrane's new block was the most important, but there were other substantial buildings, both residential and commercial.

For some years a railway from Sudbury to Manitoulin Island had been talked about, and a charter had been obtained by the Clergue interests of Sault Ste. Marie for the Manitoulin and North Shore Railway, later called the Algoma Eastern. By the middle of June, 1900, construction had been started and three miles graded from Sudbury westward. In the following years the road inched its way, providing transportation for mines such as the North Star, Creighton, Victoria, Crean Hill and Inez. Eventually it was acquired by the C.P.R., which continued to operate it from Espanola to Little Current, but the tracks between Espanola and Sudbury, duplicating the C.P.R.'s Soo line, were later removed.

Power-development on some of the nearby streams was engaging the attention of budding Sudbury capitalists. J. R. Gordon incorporated a company to develop power on the Vermilion River and offered to supply the town. Frank Cochrane and William McVittie built a plant on the Wanapitei River, and secured a contract to supply power to Sudbury and some of the mines. This plant was later sold to the Ontario Hydro-Electric Power Commission.

# IX

## *Formative Years*

SUDBURY'S CHARACTER WAS LARGELY moulded in its first decade as a town. During that period, the lines of its future were established. While lumbering still continued within a few miles of the town, bringing profitable business to its merchants, Sudbury had definitely become a mining community. Moreover, despite gold mining booms and, for a while, great excitement concerning coal, Sudbury could see itself as the coming nickel centre of the world.

The advent of the Vivians had raised hopes that the town would no longer be so largely a one-company community, but when they withdrew that hope had faded, especially since so many other promising ventures at about the same time had failed. Hope revived with the arrival of the Mond company, backed by plenty of money, and this hope was strengthened by the businesslike manner in which that company managed its affairs. Although control remained in England, the Monds were shrewd enough to take advantage of local knowledge and experience.

Nevertheless, most Sudburians were little concerned with such matters. Like most people everywhere at all times, they were occupied with making a living, with getting enough of that scarce commodity, cash, to make ends meet, each doing what he could in his own way to render Sudbury a better place to live in.

87

This was still a most pressing problem. With many new people coming into the community, and a high rate of natural increase, a continual strain was put on school facilities. Streets and sidewalks must be provided, and most of the citizens were still engaged in rooting out the great pine stumps which disfigured the landscape. During this period the waterworks and sewerage system were put in and the town was supplied with electric lights.

Men differed, as elsewhere, in politics and religion, but they were able to co-operate on community projects, and in their sports and diversions these divisions were largely forgotten. For the first time, the municipal elections on January 7, 1895, were not conducted on religious lines, and a non-Catholic, M. C. Biggar, a lawyer, was elected Mayor, while five new faces appeared in Council.

Important in developing friendly relations among the people were the frequent skating carnivals. Previous records were exceeded by one such carnival held in Martin's Skating Rink, on January 25, 1895, at which over one hundred skaters were in costume and the spectators numbered nearly two hundred and fifty. According to Jimmy Orr, "a noticeable feature was the large number of married men and their wives in costume," probably a trend of some significance at the time!

Jimmy Orr had been railing without effect against the custom of allowing horses, cattle and even hogs to roam the streets without any restriction. In one issue he tried sarcasm. "Some Pembroke people are agitating for a public park," he wrote. "A town that allows cattle to run at large and pasture on the streets hasn't much use for a park and couldn't appreciate it." And elsewhere in the same issue he returned to the subject, quoting a subscriber who wanted to know what the council proposed doing about a cow by-law. "We are unable to answer him," the editor declared, "but speaking for ourselves we would like to see a by-law passed and strictly enforced prohibiting animals of all kinds from running at large on our streets. Failing that, we at least hope that the cow bell nuisance will be abated, which of itself would be a boon to suffering humanity!" But he had a good many years of suffering ahead of him. Sudburians have always been noted for their civic pride, but it has never been manifest in the appearance of their community.

The bicycle craze had hit the town! The *Journal* reported on April 25, 1895, that "Arthur Fensom now rides a Star bicycle, and is quite an adept. This makes seven bicycles now in this section, five in Sudbury and two at Copper Cliff." The number quickly increased to include even women, among whom was Mrs. P. S. Frawley.

Meanwhile, the Council had been attempting without much success to get a contracting firm to install its utilities. The difficulty was that the town had not succeeded in selling its debentures, and must find contractors willing to accept them in payment. Finally, the contract was awarded to M. M. McCarthy of Sherbrooke, Quebec, and W. H. Plummer of Sault Ste. Marie, who agreed to accept the bonds at par. The contract price was $40,650.

In 1895, two public institutions had their inception. On October 17th, the Board of Trade was organized with the following officers: President, Frank Cochrane; 1st V.P., D. O'Connor; 2nd V.P., D. L. McKinnon; Treasurer, Jas. Purvis; Secretary, M. Allard; Council—Messrs. Fournier, Orr, Lennon, Cook, Ryan, Paul, Elliott, Gill and P. S. Frawley. It is perhaps significant that none of these was primarily interested in mining; the Board's chief concern was evidently commercial activities.

The other institution was a Public Library. In its issue of December 12th, the *Journal* contained notice of a proposed by-law for the establishment of a library under the provisions of the Public Libraries Act. The by-law was carried by a majority of fifty the following January 6th. And, on April 2nd, the *Journal* reported:

The first order for books has been given by the Board, and it is expected that the reading room will be opened about the 8th of April. A suitable room has been secured in the Johnson-Washburn block. A number of citizens have kindly offered to donate one or more volumes of standard works, and we are requested to ask that any others who contemplate assisting the board in like manner will confer a favour by notifying Mr. T. Fournier, the Librarian, to that effect at an early date. By doing so it will enable the Board to prepare a catalogue, and also prevent ordering duplicate copies.

The first contribution of books has been made by Mr. A. McCharles, about a dozen volumes, including Dr. Irving's great monograph of the copper regions of Lake Superior.

The year 1896 is notable in the annals of Sudbury as the year of the great coal boom. Someone discovered in a narrow fissure in the rocks within the Basin, a few miles north of Sudbury, a hard black substance. Samples were brought into town and tested. It was hard and shiny and certainly looked like anthracite coal; if sufficient heat were applied for a sufficient length of time it would catch fire and burn. In a forge, it produced intense heat with very little smoke. Various "experts" pronounced it to be coal. The town went wild, and prospectors rushed out to locate claims, but the coal-bearing area was limited. Nevertheless, applications for claims covering a large area were hastily dispatched to Toronto, but the government withdrew the lands from sale, and sent Dr. A. P. Coleman, geologist of the Bureau of Mines, familiar with the geology of Sudbury Basin, to examine the find.

After making his examination, Dr. Coleman was mum, and it was not till his report had been published by the Bureau that Sudbury learned that its coal mine did not contain coal at all, but a substance having the appearance of coal called anthraxolite. The veins containing the anthraxolite were in a slate formation which at a time in past geologic ages had contained a certain percentage of bitumen. The pressure and heat to which the formation had later been subjected caused some of the bitumen to collect in veins or fissures. Its composition was similar to that of anthracite, containing less volatile matter and considerable amounts of quartz and pyrites. Even so, no large deposits could be expected.

Nevertheless, a Professor Granville Cole, who claimed to be a coal expert, visited the property and reported to the company exploiting the find that it was indeed anthracite, expressing the opinion that large quantities of good coal would be found at a depth of fifty or sixty feet.

By this time the controversy was front-page news all over the province; experts bloomed everywhere. The Toronto *Globe* directed a blast at the government for having withdrawn the lands from sale:

The people of Ontario as a whole will view the action of the Government in withdrawing from sale the lands in the vicinity of the anthraxolite deposits with very different feelings from those of the settlers there. It would be folly of the worst sort to part with these lands at a nominal price to the representatives of a syndicate of sharp business men and discover a month or so later that a great fuel deposit of incalculable value had been given away for a song to be exploited by a few persons for their own aggrandizement instead of being used for the public benefit. . . .

The Kincardine *Review* gave the affair a humorous twist:

An Indian named Charcoal is in jail at Fort MacLeod awaiting death for murder. His only hope of escape rests in getting Prof. Coleman or some other expert to say that he is not Charcoal, but anthraxolite.

Jimmy Orr had gone all out in his belief that Sudbury had an undoubted coal mine, and months later continued to argue against expert opinion:

Notwithstanding the adverse opinion of geologists and would be geologists, that it was impossible to find coal here, the Citizens' Gold and Coal Company of this place believed otherwise, and during the past few months have steadily persevered in the sinking of a shaft, determined to settle the question once for all. Last week, at a depth of about 80 feet, they reached a fine bed of anthracite. . . . Since Friday last, when the first samples were brought in, there has been a great demand for stock, over 10,000 shares, we are informed, have been disposed of. The Citizens' Co. is deserving of every credit for the faith and pluck displayed, with the disadvantages of small capital and *expert professional opinion to contend against.*

Over a year later, an inconspicuous item appeared in the paper stating that the Citizens' Gold and Coal Company was offering 100,000 shares, preferably to present shareholders, at three cents a share. A later offering was made at two cents, and that was the end of Sudbury's coal boom. Sudbury Basin is a marvellous mineral storehouse, but one thing it can never produce is coal!

In the meantime, the city fathers were having difficulties with the contractors responsible for the installation of the waterworks, sewage system and electric lights. According to the contract, the work was to have been completed by October, 1895, but the Council, acting without proper advice, granted an extension of time until the end of November, thus apparently voiding a penalty clause for non-fulfilment of contract on time. The result was that the contractors then made little effort to complete the work, eventually forcing the Council to take over the job and have it completed under its own engineers.

Then, when the equipment arrived, it was not up to specification, but against the advice of the engineers the Council accepted and had it installed. The equipment proved to be much more expensive to operate than anticipated, consuming a cord of wood an hour. The dynamo and connections were secondhand, painted to look like new. Eventually it was found necessary to scrap the whole plant and install a new one, which greatly added to the capital cost, to say nothing of the further delay. The people of Sudbury were learning the hard way. They were finally to secure the services of a young man, Rex Martindale, who would take charge of their waterworks, electric light plant, and a great deal else, but before he arrived they were to have several years of inadequate equipment and incompetent supervision.

In September, 1897, Sudbury experienced a mystery which created a sensation and remained a subject of conjecture and discussion for over a year. One of the town's most prominent citizens, a lawyer and one-time mayor,

M. C. Biggar, disappeared. Although it was widely publicized in the press, no word was received of the missing man.

Following a two-day absence on business up the Soo line, he had arrived in town about eight o'clock of a Tuesday evening, going to his office after arranging with his wife to meet him there at ten o'clock. When Mrs. Biggar arrived at the office, he was not there, and after waiting some time she went home, expecting he had gone out on some unforeseen errand.

When he failed to show up later at home, she assumed that he had again gone out of town and would send her a message (this was before there were any telephones). But when no sign or word of him was received by Thursday morning, she reported his strange absence. A search party was organized. Several persons reported having seen him on Tuesday evening going in the direction of Lake Ramsey. Biggar's law clerk was camping at the time on an island in the lake and it was thought he had gone to consult the clerk, but the latter had seen nothing of him. This theory was strengthened, however, by the finding of a boat that had apparently drifted ashore about half a mile from the landing. In the boat was a piece torn from a telegram that had come to Biggar's office during his previous absence.

From this it was supposed that, attempting to row the boat out to the island, Biggar had somehow fallen out and been drowned. The lake was thoroughly searched, dynamite was exploded, dealing death and destruction to fish, but no sign of the missing man was found. Eventually, interest in the matter subsided, but Sudbury people were divided between those who believed that Biggar was drowned and those who held that he had decamped.

The latter group had reason for justification, as the sequel unfolded. In the following year, Gus Harwood, he of the 1893 election protest, was in San Francisco on his way to southern California when he unexpectedly came on Biggar in the street. The fugitive explained that he had joined the Klondike rush and was then in San Francisco

only to organize another expedition to go north.   That was
the last Sudbury ever heard of its former citizen and mayor.

The South African war did not directly affect anyone
in the Sudbury district, but many followed its course with
interest, and on March 1, 1900, the relief of Ladysmith
brought forth a spontaneous demonstration.   At seven
o'clock the fire bells rang, summoning the citizens to gather
at the vacant space near the corner of Elgin and Elm,
where a large bonfire was built and a temporary speaker's
platform erected.   Mayor T. J. Ryan presided, calling in
turn upon an array of local worthies, none of whom seems
to have held back.   The list of speakers included three
preachers and seven business and professional men, as well
as the prospector, Æneas McCharles.   Oom Paul Kruger
and his cohorts doubtless received their just desserts, and
the evening ended with fireworks and "God Save the
Queen."

J. G. Lowe, who was to be identified with education
in Sudbury for more than half a century, began teaching
in 1901, in the little frame four-room building with a stove
in every room.   J. A. Ross, the principal, having taken a
job with the Mond Nickel Company, was succeeded by
W. P. Hedley, a fellow-teacher with Lowe, and when
Hedley also left a short while later, Lowe became principal.
When Central brick school of eight rooms was opened on
the site of the present Civic Arena, Lowe was its first
principal.   After giving up teaching, he became secretary
of the High School Board.

# X

# *Inco Is Born*

Nickel, once a metallurgical nuisance, and then a novelty, had now become an important factor in the world's economy with an apparently secure and expanding future. The most serious technical problems involving its smelting and refining had seemingly been solved. But, most important of all, the Sudbury Basin had been demonstrated as an almost inexhaustible source of ores sufficiently high grade and uniform in content to justify the investment of the large sums that would be required before the nickel industry could be established on a basis comparable, for example, to that of steel.

Comparison with steel naturally suggested the amalgamation of the various nickel interests, on the pattern of the recently formed United States Steel Company. The successful flotation of that enterprise encouraged promoters to look elsewhere for similar opportunities, and also released large blocks of capital for new ventures.

Whether the initiative was taken by the steel interests or by some of those in the nickel industry is not clear, but when the scheme was completed, it was seen that steel men like Charles M. Schwab and legal firms like Sullivan & Cromwell, closely identified with the steel industry, were associated in the enterprise with Colonel Thompson and others who had pioneered the nickel industry. The

International Nickel Company, incorporated under the laws of New Jersey, brought together most of the principal concerns engaged in mining, smelting and refining nickel in both hemispheres.

The International Nickel Company had an authorized capital of $24,000,000, with power to issue bonds up to a par value of $12,000,000. The companies comprised in the consolidation were: the Orford Copper Company, the American Nickel Works (formerly operated by Joseph Wharton, Camden, N.J.), the Society Miniere Caledonienne, the Canadian Copper Company, the Anglo-American Iron Company, the Vermilion Mining Company of Ontario, Limited, Nickel Corporation Limited, a British company operating in New Caledonia and one of the promotions of the notorious Whitaker Wright, and the Huronian Company Limited, acquired shortly after the others, a Canadian Copper Company subsidiary organized to develop hydro-electric power.

So far as Canadian operations were concerned, the company's headquarters continued to be Copper Cliff, which up to 1901 had been part of the township of McKim. In that year, however, the town of Copper Cliff was incorporated. Practically all the land (1,700 acres) within the town limits and a majority of the houses were owned by the company. Most of the money spent on improvements, such as streets, waterworks, sewerage, etc., were paid for by the company. In 1902, however, Copper Cliff was a very primitive place. According to D. H. Browne:

A photograph of the company's office shows half a dozen pigs asleep under the office windows, others disputed with "Barney", Mr. Turner's dog, for the shelter of the kennel. The smelter buildings were all of wood and fires were so frequent that the insurance companies considered the probability that we might have incendiary propensities. There was no system of fire protection and when one house took fire a bucket brigade kept water on the adjoining dwellings and left the doomed building to its fate. Turner built a pretentious log cabin for himself in 1902, which was in direct contravention to his own orders that no more log shanties should be erected at Copper Cliff. The old

Club House, built in 1889, was full of bugs—not the kind Mr. Evans formerly collected. These were nocturnal, wingless and aggressive.

For three years at the turn of the century Copper Cliff was the home of an internationally known writer who, however, has left but fleeting impressions of the place. In January, 1901, Dr. Theobald Coleman arrived (in the midst of a smallpox epidemic, incidentally) to take a position as company physician, bringing with him his bride of a few months, "Kit," the famous columnist of the Toronto *Mail and Empire*, freshly back from reporting the Spanish-American war for her paper.

Although she continued her weekly article from Copper Cliff and wrote about all sorts of subjects, life in a small northern mining camp seems not to have intrigued her as a subject for her writing. There was an occasional complaint about the climate, the lack of vegetation caused by the sulphur fumes, the inconveniences of life in a primitive community and the custom of allowing pigs to roam at will. And even though in her second year she could refer to Copper Cliff as "the briskest, brightest mining town in Ontario if not in Canada," there is little doubt that at the end of her husband's term she left the "briskest, brightest mining town" without the least regret.

A. P. Turner, who first saw Copper Cliff in 1899, in a reminiscent mood, wrote:

The old office building at Copper Cliff was a small frame building which in winter time was so cold as to be almost unbearable. It was heated with a baseburner, and a small stove in the private office; and many times no work could be done until after 11 o'clock on account of no heat. Later, steam pipes were brought into the office from the Copper Cliff boilers. It was supposed to be heated by the exhaust steam from the boilers, but this method did not work very well on account of the back pressures. . . . Another of the great economies that was attempted at Copper Cliff was the maintenance of a central heating plant. This was installed at the time the hospital was built, and in addition to heating the office and the hospital heated several of the superintendents' houses. This, however, was not successful as all the users of the steam threw open the windows of their houses when it became hot, but the boilers in the central heating plant worked on just the same whether the weather was hot or cold.[1]

Dr. Peters, with James McArthur and J. D. Evans as assistants, was in charge at Copper Cliff when smelting began. Peters resigned in 1890, and after a short interval was succeeded by Evans, who continued until 1893. McArthur then became manager, continuing in the post until after the amalgamation, when A. P. Turner became president of the Canadian Copper Company and manager at Copper Cliff.

Since 1888, when the first smelter was blown in, Copper Cliff had become an active smelting centre. New furnaces were added from time to time as ore production increased. In 1889 the West smelter, near Mine No. 2, was blown in, establishing a new smelting centre. The East smelter, the first established, burned down about the time of the amalgamation.

While room still remained for improvements in smelting and refining, the processes already evolved could be counted on to produce nickel enough to meet a much greater demand than was then apparent. But, not satisfied with the matte they were receiving at Constable Hook from the Canadian Copper Company, the Orford Copper Company in 1900 built the Ontario Smelting Works (about half a mile south-west of the Copper Cliff mine) to produce a higher grade matte. Accepting delivery of the Canadian Copper Company's thirty to thirty-five per cent matte, the Ontario Smelting Works, by roasting it in Brown calciners and resmelting in a water-jacket furnace, converted it into matte having an average of about seventy-five per cent combined nickel and copper.

At the time of the amalgamation the Canadian Copper Company was operating five mines, the Frood, McArthur (No. 2), Creighton, Copper Cliff, Vermilion; and owned six others, Nos. 4, 5 (McAllister) and 6, Stobie and Evans, all

[1]From an unpublished manuscript.

of which had previously been operated, but were then closed down. In addition, it owned or controlled several thousand acres of undeveloped property in various parts of the Sudbury district.

Since it was estimated that ore reserves in mines owned by the Canadian Copper Company were sufficient to feed its furnaces for at least sixty years, and the company controlled only a small fraction of the Sudbury field, ore supply was clearly no problem.

In 1889 the tonnage mined in the Sudbury area was 44,490, of which 40,146 tons were treated. In 1891, tonnage mined had increased to 83,300, of which 72,558 tons were treated for 10,336 tons of matte, producing respectively 2,018 tons of nickel and 2,064 tons of copper. Between 1891 and 1900, the advance, though fluctuating, was gradual, the nickel content of ore produced in the latter year being 3,540 tons.

A. P. Turner has written that when, as a young man, he became an employee of the Canadian Copper Company in Cleveland what most impressed him was that the company owed the bank $200,000. This was indicative of the company's financial position. Needed improvements were always deferred until the last possible moment because of lack of money, and when finally undertaken were often inadequate.

Now, with ample working capital, the first efforts of the management were devoted to plant rehabilitation and improvement. At Copper Cliff a move was made to smarten up and bring into semblance of order the heterogeneous collection of shacks and other structures that had resulted from the makeshift policy of the past, and it would not be many years before an impressive transformation had taken place.

The pressing need, however, was to increase the consumption of nickel, although this was now no longer the exclusive concern of the Canadian management. But upon an increase in nickel sales the fate of the nickel industry depended, and with it the fate of the Sudbury mines.

It must be remembered that nickel was still considered a new metal, its value and utility not very widely appreciated, although recent recognition by the leading countries of the world of its effectiveness for armour plate had meant a considerable step forward. Yet if it was to assume the place in the world's economy envisaged by the few who realized its qualities, many more uses must be found for the metal.

Turner tells of his early efforts to interest manufacturers and others in its use:

I remember that almost my first employment with the company was addressing letters to different manufacturers explaining how their work could be benefited by the use of nickel as an alloy. Letters were addressed to manufacturers of steel plate, chain, axes, etc. This correspondence was seriously interrupted by receiving a letter from the Cramp Shipbuilding Company that they had tried to use nickel in the manufacture of their steel plates for boilers, but could not use it on account of its blistering, and our experience with nickel-steel up to that time was such that we could not give them very much good advice. . . . It is questionable how much good this correspondence did, but I know there were a great many enquiries to our letters, and occasionally an order for nickel developed.

The most significant feature of the amalgamation was that the nickel industry became even more than ever an adjunct to the United States economy, especially the steel industry. The value of nickel as an alloy for steel was fully recognized by the shrewd men in the steel business; but steel manufacture was centred in the United States, not in Canada, and that would be the situation for a good many years. When a nickel-steel mill was erected at Carnegie's Homestead works, it was for the primary purpose of supplying armour plate for the U.S. navy.

While this situation was inevitable in view of Canada's limited demand for nickel, it had a disquieting effect in some Canadian quarters. Although the Canadian Copper Company, despite its United States management and ownership, had seemed a Canadian concern, the implications of this new alignment could not be overlooked. There had always been the prospect that the company would eventually fulfil its obligation to complete its refining process in Canada, but with Colonel Thompson and his new-found friends in control that prospect seemed much more remote.

On the other hand, there was evidence that even before the amalgamation the nickel industry was considered by the owners of the Canadian Copper Company as an adjunct of the United States economy. In 1896, President Burke had warned the Ways and Means Committee of the House of Representatives at Washington that,

the putting of a duty upon either nickel ore or nickel matte would result necessarily in the refining of this product in Canada, or in Great Britain, or in Germany.

And he added:

We have preferred to have this work done in this country. We have preferred to give our people the benefit of it.

All of which was quite natural.

Therefore, one of the chief duties of the Canadian management after amalgamation was to combat the efforts of those who, by one means or another, were attempting to force the company to refine in Canada. It would take a world war to bring this about, and in the meantime, the fact that he was able to defer the inevitable was counted by A. P. Turner as not the least of his achievements in the interest of his company.

One of the principal improvements made possible by the merger was the change at Copper Cliff from acid to basic converters. The original furnaces, built of steel, were lined with an eighteen-inch thickness of clay mixed with quartz. Since quartz is a fluxing material, such linings lasted only about eighteen hours, during which not more than five tons of bessemer matte could be produced before the furnace must be relined.

In the meantime, basic (non-silicious) linings had been adopted successfully elsewhere, and beginning in March,

1911, the ten acid furnaces at Copper Cliff were replaced by five basic converters. To take the place of the flux previously supplied by the lining, sufficient silicious material was added to provide a flux for the iron in the charge. (When the Mond Nickel Company built its smelter at Coniston in 1913, basic converters were installed at the outset.)

The next step at Copper Cliff was the installation of reverberatory furnaces for the smelting of flue dust and finely ground sulphides (called "fines"), which ordinary blast furnaces cannot handle. (Mond, on the other hand, adopted the method of sintering (semi-roasting by means of ignited sulphur) to consolidate the fines into a form acceptable as furnace feed).

The cost of fuel was always an important factor, and Inco shortly after the amalgamation undertook to supply its mines and plants with electric power. Under a sub-sidiary, the Huronian Company, Limited, power rights were secured at High Falls on Spanish River, about twenty-eight miles west of Copper Cliff, where a natural sixty-seven-foot head was obtainable. A dam raised this to eighty-five feet and provided a reservoir for water storage. This was the first of several hydro-electric installations which the company was to undertake as its requirements increased.

# XI

# *Brave New Century*

SUDBURY WAS SEVENTEEN YEARS OLD WHEN the new century dawned, and the community's chief characteristics were already well established. Outstanding among these was a love for sports—skating, curling, hockey, baseball and lacrosse. At that time the Sudbury Curling Club was a member of the Northern International Curling Association, comprising clubs at Mattawa, North Bay, Chapleau, Sault Ste. Marie, Ontario, and Sault Ste. Marie, Michigan. Although for years the rivalry between the Sudbury and North Bay hockey clubs was intense, it was mild in comparison with that between Sudbury and Copper Cliff. Before motor cars, when infrequent trains were the only means of transport, players and large numbers of supporters (the word "fans" was not yet coined) travelled long distances to attend bonspiels and hockey matches.

Jimmy Orr was a devoted curler and saw that the *Journal* carried full accounts of every match and bonspiel, but he also was careful to see that other sports were well covered. A typical account of a lacrosse game between Sudbury and Copper Cliff appeared in the issue of June 21, 1900 (it will be noted that the modern sports writer's touch is lacking):

What is generally admitted to have been the best lacrosse match ever played in this town took place on Wednesday afternoon between the Sudbury and Copper Cliff teams. It was good lacrosse throughout, with very little unnecessary rough play. Two of the players, Porter and Ritchie, accidentally struck their heads together, knocking them out for a few minutes.

Nets were used at the flags for the first time here, and they certainly are a decided improvement on the old method, which so often caused wrangling and disputing in the past. When a game is scored now there can be no disputing it. . . .

Where everyone in both teams played so well it is scarcely fair to single out anyone for special mention, but we may be permitted to remark especially on the excellent work done by the Copper Cliff goal keeper, W. Dorsett. Shot after shot was dead in the flags, and while he could not be expected to keep all out, he certainly succeeded in keeping out a large number.

This item is of especial interest because of the mention of Will Dorsett, for more than half a century one of Sudbury's most ardent sports devotees. While lacrosse was his favourite, he was almost as fond of hockey, and in his later years has been a constant and enthusiastic curler. At the time of the game reported above, he was serving his apprenticeship as a jeweller in the Copper Cliff store of J. S. Gill. Eventually succeeding his employer, he was for many years prominent in the business life of Sudbury, and his retirement a few years ago has provided time for him to devote greater attention to his favourite sports, either as player or spectator.

It was not till 1910 that a golf club was formed, which is not surprising considering the Sudbury terrain. In later years the Sudbury golf course would become noted for its excellence, and Sudbury golfers among the most enthusiastic members of a fraternity certainly not lacking in enthusiasm. The Sudbury Boating Club was organized in 1902, and in 1912 a clubhouse twenty-four by ninety-six feet was built at Lake Ramsey. The first regatta was held that summer.

Before the movies arrived, when travelling companies provided the only means of theatrical entertainment, Sudbury was noted as a show town much in advance of others of its size. In 1902, George H. Lennon converted a three-storey brick building on Cedar Street, midway between Durham and Elgin streets, into an "opera house" capable of staging any of the companies which came to the town. It had a stage twenty by thirty feet and the auditorium had seats for 650, with provision for another 200 in the gallery.

In 1908 the Grand Theatre was built at the corner of Beech and Elgin Streets, a much more pretentious place which served the community for many years and, now devoted to the movies, still does.

Sudburians were not wholly bent upon amusement; they were keenly interested in whatever might promote the welfare of their town. They kept a close watch on the doings of the Council and took an increasing interest in provincial and federal politics, in both of which Sudbury men were to become noted.

From the time he had arrived from Mattawa in 1890 to take over the hardware store of D. R. McPhail, Frank Cochrane had been one of the town's leading citizens. Elected to the Council in 1896, he became mayor in 1897 and served for several terms. His first attempt in politics failed when he ran in 1902 as Conservative candidate in Nipissing West, but upon the Whitney government's attaining office in 1905 he was appointed Minister of Lands and Mines. Charles Lamarche, member for Nipissing East, resigned to provide a seat, to which Cochrane was elected by acclamation. In 1911 he accepted the post of Minister of Railways in the Borden government, which he held until the formation of the Union government in 1917.

A few months before his appointment as Minister of Mines in the Whitney cabinet, Cochrane, returning to Sudbury on a C.P.R. train, had alighted for a moment at Wanapitei station, and while getting back on board he slipped under the wheels, which mangled his right leg so badly that amputation below the knee was necessary.

Cochrane's transfer from the provincial field provided an opportunity for another of Sudbury's rising citizens. On July 25, 1901, the *Journal* had carried an inconspicuous item to the effect that "Mr. Charles McCrea, who came here from Renfrew a few weeks ago to enter Mr. Clary's

law office, did not succeed in making arrangements as
expected, and is now in charge of a branch office opened
here by Messrs. McGarry & Devine, barristers, of Renfrew." Three months later another item recorded that
"Mr. Charles McCrea branches out this week as a barrister,
solicitor, etc.," and from then on his name appeared
frequently in connection with public affairs. When Frank
Cochrane moved to Ottawa in 1911, McCrea was elected
to the legislature in his place, and eventually also became
Minister of Mines.

In January, 1902, after a preliminary investigation, a
representative of the Bell Telephone Company recommended the installation of telephones in Sudbury and
Copper Cliff, and shortly afterward the company applied
to the Council for the exclusive right for five years to string
its wires along streets and lanes.

The Council voted against a franchise, but authorized
Mayor Frank Cochrane to inform the company that in
consideration of its giving the town free use of two instru-
ments for a year, one at the firehall and the other at the
powerhouse, the company's taxes would be remitted during
that period. With this the company was forced to be
content. Shortly after the middle of April, the system
was in operation. Over sixty subscribers had been secured
in Sudbury and thirty in Copper Cliff. "Central" was at
H. S. Young's drug store.

Relations with the Canadian Pacific Railway, never very
cordial, were particularly unpleasant during this period.
The company took the view that, since its line from
Montreal to Vancouver passed through Sudbury, and it
owned the land adjacent to its station and had laid out a
townsite, it had a right to sell lots or not as it saw fit. The
citizens of Sudbury now looked upon the railway as a
convenient source of revenue, even objecting because the
company's trains crossed some of their streets.

On the other hand, the citizens felt that they had good
cause for complaint. They said the company's officers
treated them with scant courtesy, making repeated

promises that were not kept. The company's lands, comprising about five hundred acres, constituted the main portion of the town, yet persons desiring lots for homes or businesses were often denied a chance to buy, thus being forced to go farther from the business centre. This interfered with the orderly laying out of improvements, increasing their cost as well. Despite many promises to improve them, facilities for both passengers and freight were woefully inadequate.

In 1895, the Council and the C.P.R. had come to an agreement concerning the assessment value of the company's property, which was set at $14,000 to hold for five years. At the end of this period, the assessor had raised the assessment to $59,000, but the company appealed. Superintendent C. W. Spencer offered, as a compromise, to accept a valuation of $20,000 if the town would not increase it during the next five years. At the same time, Mr. Spencer renewed the promise, made many times before, to build a new station and remove the freight shed to a more convenient location. The Council, sceptical of these promises, agreed to the $20,000 valuation, but only for one year as a test of the company's sincerity.

Mr. Spencer now refused this offer and the case went to the Court of Revision, which raised the assessment to $25,000 to run for five years, contingent upon the company's spending between $40,000 and $50,000 on a new station and freight shed, removal of its tracks from the east to the west side of the station, and the installation of a much-needed crossing.

On November 7, 1901, nearly a year and a half later, the *Journal* had given vent to this complaint:

Almost every businessman in town is complaining loudly of the manner in which the C.P.R. authorities are treating their patrons in this place. It seems almost impossible to get freight delivered in reasonable time after its arrival. Several have drawn our attention to this state of affairs during the past two or three weeks. Parties with carloads of goods consigned have had to wait a week before they could get their car placed in a

position to unload.   It is not the fault of the officials here.
So far as we know they are obliging and willing to do all they can,
but the plain fact appears to be that the company is too penurious
to send enough men here to do the work properly.   Neither in the
freight shed or yard is there sufficient help.   We believe more
freight is received here and shipped from Sudbury than from any
other station between Montreal and Vancouver, with the exception of Ottawa and Winnipeg, and not counting the grain business
at Fort William.   And yet their station and shed accommodation
is about the very worst on the line.   They appear to think "any
old thing" is good enough for Sudbury.   The station is simply a
disgrace to the town as well as to the company.   A new one has
been promised for years, and special reduction made in their
assessment on account of such promises, but their promises are
quickly forgotten as soon as they secure what privileges they
ask for.

The next chapter in the C.P.R. serial began in April,
1905, with the announcement that Sudbury was to be made
a divisional point and that a station of pressed brick costing
$35,000 and large enough to accommodate all the necessary
offices was to be built.   Certain streets would need to be
closed on account of the railway yards, but the company
promised that its vacant property would be surveyed and
put on sale.   In return for this, and in view of the amount
of money to be spent, estimated at $300,000, the company
asked that its assessment be set at $50,000 for a term of
years.

The Council, by now wary of promises, would not agree
to the suggested assessment; and after some further
negotiation the company agreed to an assessment of
$100,000, with the understanding that it would not be
increased for five years.   But in spite of this agreement the
C.P.R. in 1906 entered an appeal, which the Court of
Revision and the District Judge both declined to consider.
Finally, on September 6, 1907, the new station was opened.

In the meantime, the company had begun in earnest the
construction of its branch between Toronto and Sudbury.
In November, 1905, report had it that the first rails would
be laid in a few days at Bolton; in the following April,

announcement was made that a contract for the fifty-seven-mile section from Parry Sound to Byng Inlet had been awarded; and work was proceeding all along the line. On June 14, 1908, the first passenger train from Toronto reached Sudbury. This recital might be concluded with the announcement made in August, 1912, that the C.P.R. would shortly begin work on a $25,000 office building on the corner of Elm and Elgin streets. (The building was completed on time and, later enlarged, is still in use.)

Sudbury now had the long-expected railway to Toronto, and was soon to have another. Mackenzie & Mann, builders of the Canadian Northern Railway in the West, had acquired the charter of the James Bay Railway which for years remained nothing more than a charter. Whether it should finally be built and where depended largely upon its promoters' success in securing subsidies. In consideration of promises to build into Sudbury, a deputation of Sudbury businessmen, accompanied by the local member, C. A. McCool, had gone to Ottawa to assist Mackenzie & Mann in getting a federal subsidy. They were assured that the charter had been amended specifically to include entry into Sudbury.

Toward the end of 1905, however, Sudbury people learned to their dismay that the charter had been re-amended (or not altered in the first place), and that the James Bay Railway was planning to by-pass Sudbury, merely serving the town by a spur from a point several miles to the east. At a public meeting, Mayor Larry O'Connor and Wm. McVittie were appointed to go to Toronto and interview Mackenzie & Mann.

The deputation saw Donald Mann, who assured them that the reports were incorrect and that the James Bay Railway was indeed being built into Sudbury. The chief difficulty, he said, was finding a suitable route through the hills to the south, but he promised to send another engineer to make a further examination of the terrain. Nevertheless, Sudburians learned in June, 1906, that the railway (later known as the Canadian Northern Ontario Railway) would by-pass the town after all. The truth was that Mackenzie & Mann were more interested just then in building into the Moose Mountain iron mines at Hutton, about thirty miles northeast of Sudbury, owned in part by them, than in gaining an entry into Sudbury. However, on June 6, 1908, the first C.N.R. train from Toronto reached Sudbury by way of Sudbury Junction, five miles east of the town, and with this the Sudbury people had to be content.

In 1890, while Sudbury was still a village, the Bank of Ontario had opened a branch, thus securing a monopoly of the banking business. The manager, A. J. Macdonnell, was popular and took part in all village activities. In March, 1899, the Traders' Bank came to Sudbury, and business seemed ample for both. In 1901, the Bank of Toronto opened a branch in Copper Cliff, and the following year opened one in Sudbury. These new banking facilities were largely the result of increased mining activity. The failure of the Bank of Ontario, in 1906, due to the defalcation of its general manager, might have had serious consequences in Sudbury but for the prompt announcement that the Bank of Montreal had taken it over and that all deposits were guaranteed by that reliable institution. And that was how the Bank of Montreal came to Sudbury.

The Royal Bank came in somewhat the same way when it took over the business of the Traders' Bank. The Bank of Nova Scotia came *via* the Bank of Ottawa. The Canadian Bank of Commerce seems to have come on its own account, but subsequently absorbed two smaller institutions having branches in Sudbury. Banque de Hochelaga opened in 1917 and after the amalgamation with Banque Nationale has carried on under the name Banque Canadienne Nationale. The Imperial and the Dominion both arrived in 1929.

Martin's skating rink, situated on the west side of Durham, between Cedar and Larch, which held such pleasant associations for a generation of Sudburians, was torn down in the spring of 1903, and the Sudbury Rink

Company was organized to provide a successor. The new rink was opened for skaters on New Year's Day, 1904, lights for the curling section not yet being ready.

Another landmark disappeared when the National Hotel, on Elm, just west of the White House, was totally destroyed on June 2, 1904. The fire brigade, although unable to save the hotel, succeeded in confining the flames to the one building. The gap in the hotel ranks was filled the following year, when the King Edward was formally opened.

Associated with the National Hotel, which was built by D. Rothschild in 1890, is one of Sudbury's "characters." John Bidgood, self-styled "Jack the Ripper," its final proprietor, was supposed to have arrived in Sudbury from the Klondike with $30,000, which may or may not have been true. He was a man of riotous imagination and undoubtedly cut a wide swath in Sudbury.

During the latter part of 1904, granolithic sidewalks were laid along the principal business streets, and the cost assessed against the properties thus improved. These were a great advance over the former rickety board walks, or plain mud paths.

In August, 1906, R. Martin, who from Sudbury's earliest days had operated a shoe store at the corner of Larch and Durham, sold out to F. M. Stafford, who was to continue as one of the town's leading merchants (The Twin Stores) until the business was acquired by Canadian Department Stores (T. Eaton Co.), who still occupy the site.

Despite the financial panic of 1907, repercussions of which reached Sudbury, money was forthcoming for the establishment of a brewery. In that year, J. J. Mackey, his sister Mrs. George Fee and John J. Doran, former proprietor of the English Chop House, Toronto, selected a site on the Copper Cliff road and built there a three-storey brick building which was said to contain the most modern of beer-making equipment. In good times and bad, the brewery has prospered.

Those who had refused to become excited a few years earlier when other towns were competing for the honour of being the seat of the judicial district were now justified, for in April, 1907, the government established the judicial district of Sudbury without any balloting or other formalities, and Judge J. J. Kehoe, of Sault Ste. Marie, was appointed the first judge.

Sudbury had long ago reached the stage when a high school was badly needed. Those who could afford it had been sending their sons and daughters to boarding schools in the cities, while less fortunate folk did without secondary education. During 1907, however, the efforts of a small group of stalwarts were rewarded and steps were taken to provide high school instruction in Sudbury itself. Pending construction of a high school building, temporary quarters were secured in the Jubilee Hall, corner of Durham and Beech, and on January 6, 1908, the first classes were called to order by Principal Davidson and his assistants Misses Adie and MacKenzie. By the fall of 1909 the building had been completed, and it was opened on September 7th with over one hundred students. Mr. Wethy had been added to the staff, which still included Mr. Davidson and Misses Adie and MacKenzie, who are remembered in the names of streets near the school. Three years later, technical classes, including instruction in practical mining, were added.

On Sunday, January 5, 1908, the Methodists, who for twenty-one years had worshipped in a little frame building on Beech Street which the congregation had far outgrown, dedicated their new building on Cedar at Lisgar Street. It had accommodation for five hundred, and was in every way a credit to those who planned and built it. Unfortunately it burned down some years later, and on the site the Bell Telephone Company built its business office and Central Exchange.

A second weekly newspaper, the *Mining News*, published from time to time by J. F. and A. Templeton, had offered competition to the *Journal;* but now Sudbury was deemed of sufficient importance to justify a daily.    Publication of the first number was postponed from time to time, but on January 14, 1909, the *Northern Star* made its appearance, claiming to be the only morning paper between Toronto and the North Pole.    It was an eight-page, seven-column paper, "established solely for the purpose of serving the people and interests of New Ontario, first, last and all the time."    The managing editor was G. J. Ashworth, late of the Toronto *Star.*

In June the *Northern Star* suspended publication for lack of capital, and this brought to the fore a man who, until his death in 1948, was to be actively identified with Sudbury's affairs.    William E. Mason, born in Bruce County, Ontario, in 1882, had been employed in the printing shop of Toronto *Saturday Night* before coming to Sudbury in November, 1907, to take charge of the *Star's* composing room.    After the paper's failure under its previous management, a group of thirteen Sudbury businessmen pledged a sum eventually amounting to $6,500 to get it started again.    Mason, who had had no editorial experience, was asked if he would carry on as manager, which he undertook to do.    With a reduced staff, and publishing semi-weekly for a while, and then three times a week, Mason at length succeeded in putting the paper on its feet, and in time became sole owner.

Since Sudbury had passed the quarter-century mark, a group of oldtimers decided that the time had come for a reunion.    Dr. Howey, as the "oldest" oldtimer, was chosen chairman, and R. W. De Morest, secretary.    All males whose residence preceded the first of January, 1893, were considered eligible, and on April 30, 1909, about ninety of them gathered at a banquet in the Balmoral Hotel dining-room.    Invitations had been sent to 185 who were still residents, and 500 who had moved away.    Death had claimed 118, otherwise eligible.    One to whom all paid honour, "Squire" James McCormick—one of the first to reach Sudbury in 1883—died on September 22, 1910, in his eighty-first year.

The Palace Skating and Curling Rink, opened on New Year's Day, 1904, was completely destroyed by fire on September 26, 1910. At the annual meeting of the company a few weeks later, a majority of the shareholders voted to divide the assets and wind up the company, but a considerable number were of the opinion that the company should continue to carry out the purpose for which it had been organized, and rebuild the rink. It was finally agreed that those who wished to continue might buy the site for $1,800, and a committee was appointed to proceed with plans for a new rink. (It was opened January 3, 1913.)

It would be interesting to compile a history of a community like Sudbury in terms of its fires. The total cost of fires over a period of years would undoubtedly be found to exceed the assessed value of the surviving property. On January 16, 1912, Inco's fine hospital at Copper Cliff was totally destroyed. It was fortunate that the fire started some distance from the main part of the building, allowing time for the removal of the eleven patients. The superintendent, Dr. W. A. McCauley, the matron, and other members of the staff, whose quarters were on the second floor, lost many of their personal effects.

In May of the same year, the three-storey brick warehouse and stock of Young & Company Limited, wholesale grocers and provision merchants, on Cedar Street, were completely destroyed. This narrative could have been dotted with such accounts. Those cited will serve as a reminder that in most communities fire continues to be a largely avoidable expense.

Community developments were a reflection of increasing activity at the mines, for Sudbury had no other source of sustenance. The increase was probably more marked at the time at the Mond properties, which since 1905 had been under the local direction of C. V. Corless, previously a lecturer at McGill University.

The smelter at the Victoria mine proving inadequate, plans were made in 1910 for the building of a larger one at Coniston (completed 1913). It was well located with

An Expectant Moment in the Civic Arena

respect to railways, about eight miles east of Sudbury, and five miles south of the Garson mine from which the company was by now securing the bulk of its ore.

The Monds seemed always to fear that some day their ore supply would become endangered, and accordingly in 1911 the Frood Extension, about nine miles from Coniston, was bought, and in 1913 the Levack, in the north range about thirty miles to the northwest, was also acquired.

During this period the company adopted the use of electric power, and a first plant was built on the Vermilion River, followed by a second at Nairn Falls on the Spanish River.

By now the traffic problem had made its appearance. At its meeting on June 10, 1912 the Council (Mayor: J. G. Henry; Councillors: J. A. Mulligan, W. J. Bell, T. E. Smith, R. Martin, F. A. Ricard and George Tuddenham) took action to curb the speed of horses, automobiles and motorcycles, especially over bridges and street crossings. That horses were included with motor vehicles suggests that the city fathers had little idea of what the traffic problem was soon to become.

On July 29, 1912, Bishop Thornloe, of the diocese of Algoma, laid the corner stone of the Church of the Epiphany, on Larch Street; and on April 27th of the following year the church was dedicated by the bishop, marking the end of the Anglican Church's first quarter-century in Sudbury. Rev. Charles Piercy, who arrived on May 31, 1890, was the first resident Anglican clergyman, service having previously been conducted by Rev. Gowan Gillmor of North Bay, mentioned by Mrs. Howey. Rev. James Boydell served the Anglicans of Sudbury for many years and was one of the town's most distinguished citizens.

In view of the number of Roman Catholics in the district and the emphasis which Catholics place upon the relationship between religion and education, it was not strange that they should wish to have an educational institution in northern Ontario that would prepare students for the university under religious influence; and on August 25,

1913, the corner stone of Sacred Heart College (Jesuit) was laid by Bishop Scollard in the presence of a large number of people of all denominations. Since affiliated with Ottawa University, it has now attained university status.

What had already become and would continue to be a sore point with many citizens came to a head on October 12th, when at a meeting of the Sudbury Horticultural Society a committee was appointed to discuss with the Council and Board of Trade the advisability of calling a public meeting to consider the question of sulphur fumes from the smelter at Copper Cliff. A wide difference of opinion existed as to the actual amount of damage being done by the fumes, and the question would find its way to the courts before a more satisfactory procedure was evolved for assessing the damage.

The Sulphur Fumes Arbitration Act of the Ontario legislature later provided for the appointment of an arbitrator with authority to take evidence and make awards which are not subject to appeal, and since then claims have generally been settled amicably.

Sudbury was growing steadily; assessor Loney announced in April that the total assessment for 1913 would be $2,585,783, an increase over the previous year of $524,205. The population was estimated at 6,494, an increase of 1,438 during the year.

In 1905 Alex Brunet, a stage line operator, became the first to make use of a motor car in carrying passengers between Sudbury and Copper Cliff. His car was driven by steam and carried ten passengers and the driver. By the spring of 1913 Sudbury and Copper Cliff had about ninety automobiles of various kinds, and people were talking about a street railway. A company called the Sudbury-Copper Cliff Suburban Electric Railway Company, headed by J. R. Gordon, had been organized and was negotiating with the Council for a franchise.

The route later adopted began at Lake Ramsey, at the corner of Elizabeth and John streets, thence along John, Nelson, Station (now part of Elgin), Durham, Cedar,

Lisgar, Elm, Durham North, Beech and Notre Dame to the town limits.   The Copper Cliff branch began at the corner of Elm and Lisgar, proceeding along Elm, Lorne and Copper Cliff Road to the corner of Balsam and Power in Copper Cliff.

On some of the streets, when construction began, pine stumps were unearthed that had been covered by pavement and were so tightly embedded that it was necessary to take them out in pieces; but by the middle of July the work was well in hand, and it was expected that the cars would be running before winter.   The line was not in operation by winter, however, nor by the following spring.   World War I had broken out, and the company had failed to float its bonds.

On May 3, 1915 the company, through its solicitor, Charles McCrea, came to the Council with the request that the town guarantee $100,000 of the company's bonds for twenty years.   It was disclosed that although the promoters and others interested had subscribed $64,600, only a small part of this had been paid in.   Mayor Larry O'Connor shrewdly suggested that if these subscriptions were made good, a proposal to guarantee $75,000 of bonds might be considered.

Mr. McCrea finally accepted this offer, and a by-law authorizing such a guarantee was carried by a substantial majority of the taxpayers on June 14, 1915.   Construction was then resumed, and on November 11th an hourly service was begun between Sudbury and Copper Cliff.   The fare was fifteen cents (eight tickets for a dollar), twenty-five cents return.

# XII

# *Sudbury and World War I*

AS ELSEWHERE IN CANADA, THE WAR CAME
as an unexpected shock to Sudbury
people. For a dozen years newspapers had been featuring
war scares, but nothing had come of them, and most people
refused to get excited over the shooting of an Austrian
prince in what seemed but another Balkan squabble.
When, however, Sir Robert Borden cabled Canada's offer
to stand with the Empire, most Sudburians were in agreement; but among the *Canadien* population the enthusiasm
was not so great as with those of British birth, especially
those of more recent arrival.

For some years Sudbury had been the headquarters of a
company of the 97th Regiment, Algonquin Rifles, which at
the outbreak of the war was commanded by Major W. J.
Cressey, a printer and part owner of the Sudbury *Journal*.
As soon as war was declared, Major Cressey and his officers,
as well as most of the men in the ranks, offered their services
to the Department of Militia. Among the officers were:
Captains J. D. Glover, R. R. McKessock, J. Handley, and
Lieuts. Thomson, Baycroft, Fleming and Hall.

Within a week the Department had accepted the offer of
125 men, but double that number responded. Consequently, on August 20, 1914, a special train bound for
Valcartier, Quebec, pulled out of Sudbury with 250 men
of the 97th on board and ten officers. Major Cressey
was in command, and with him were Captains Glover,

Handley, R. Robinson and P. G. Ferguson, and Lieuts. Morgan, Peterman and McKee. Despite a heavy downpour of rain, a large number of people went to the station to see this first contingent of Sudbury soldiers depart on a mission the end of which none could foresee.

On September 4th a group of about seventy citizens, mostly women, gathered in the Court House under the chairmanship of Dr. R. H. Arthur to organize the Sudbury branch of the Canadian Patriotic Fund to provide assistance for the dependants of soldiers overseas and for other war purposes. In the early years of the war no provision was made by the Militia Department for soldiers' dependants. Large sums of money were to pass through the hands of the Fund during the next few years.

Meanwhile, after a short period at Valcartier, Sudbury's contingent had been transferred to England where, at Salisbury Plain they had received training before an early departure for the front. Major Cressey returned in December for transfer to another unit, eventually going over as second in command of the 36th Battalion, which was recruited at Hamilton.

Despite the war, life went on very much as usual in Sudbury and surrounding communities. The world, having no experience of a large-scale war, had at first been thrown into an economic panic, and prices of nearly all commodities, even those that soon would be in great demand, dropped below the cost of production. Factories were shut down and thousands of men were thrown on the labour market; large numbers found the donning of a uniform the only means of obtaining food, clothing and a roof over their heads. The depression that had settled over the country after the outbreak of war continued in the spring of 1915, and James O'Reilly opened a lunch room near the corner of Durham and Elm to provide cheap meals for those who were out of work. A "good clean meal" could be had from O'Reilly for "from five cents up."

A considerable amount of building was in progress when the war began, most of which was continued. Of chief importance was the new federal building containing the post office and local offices for the Customs and Inland Revenue departments. After much discussion and delay, the first sod had been turned on October 1, 1913, at the corner of Durham and Elm, on the site once occupied by the C.P.R. store. The site had a frontage of thirty-five feet on Elm, fifty-nine feet across the corner (cut off by the former Stobie branch railway), and sixty-eight feet on Durham. Because of the railway tracks its shape was pentagonal. The stone building was completed in the fall of 1915 at a cost of $125,000, and formally opened on November 18th by Hon. Frank Cochrane.

A tower surmounted the building and in it was a clock with four illuminated faces fitted with opal glass, each looking out on one of the four cardinal points. The clock mechanism, located in a small room immediately under the tower, was connected with the hands by steel rods leading upward through the ceiling. The time and striking mechanisms were operated by weights, the former weighing 120 and the latter 180 pounds, with a drop of ninety feet to the bottom of a well provided for the purpose.

The four cast-iron dials were six feet in diameter, lit by electric bulbs from behind. The minute hand was three feet long, and the hour hand two and a half feet. The six-foot pendulum weighed sixty pounds. The bell, three feet in diameter by three feet, four inches in height, weighed approximately eight hundred pounds, and two generations of Sudburians can bear witness to its melodiousness. A perfect timepiece, it was manufactured by J. B. Joyce & Co., of Whitechurch, Shropshire, England, builders of clocks for two centuries, and installed by Alex Beath, veteran jeweller and watchmaker of Sudbury.

Among other building projects at the beginning of the war was an extension of the Cochrane block at the corner of Durham and Cedar, finished in 1915. Also, in that year, McCormick's hall, at the corner of Elgin and Elm, was torn down, and a two-storey stone structure was built on the site which became the property of the Canadian

Bank of Commerce when the latter absorbed a smaller bank. Another landmark, also built in 1915, was the brick building to serve as a liquor store for D. Rothschild & Co. It now provides the same service under the auspices of the Liquor Control Board of Ontario.

Before the outbreak of war, D. M. Morin, proprietor of the Balmoral Hotel, had also become the proprietor of the White House through his marriage to Mrs. J. S. Miller, widow of the former owner, and had decided to tear down the hotel, building a new one in its place to be known as the Nickel Range Hotel. This plan he carried out. The new hotel, a modern five-storey structure, said to be the last word in hotel architecture and construction, was formally opened in June, 1915, by a grand ball to which over three hundred invitations were issued. That it has held its place in the estimation of the travelling public during almost forty years is a tribute both to its builder and to its management in the interval.

The first Sudbury man to lose his life in the war was Captain J. D. Glover, word of whose death was received in April, 1915. Born near Orillia, Ontario, he was only twenty-six years old when he died. For a while it was feared that Captain R. R. McKessock had also been killed, but it was later learned that he was a prisoner of war in Germany. The first Sudbury-born soldier killed in the war was Private John Gutcher.

With the new post office, Sudbury was to have a new postmaster, the fourth since the town began. The first was Stephen Fournier, who held the office till 1897, when he turned it over to J. M. Kelly. After Mr. Kelly's death, his widow had been made postmistress, but by 1915 the office had risen in importance, and Mrs. Kelly was succeeded by John McLeod, formerly in the dry goods business, but apparently having the necessary political qualifications. This left an opening for A. P. McLeod, brother of the new postmaster, who succeeded to the dry goods business.

Recruiting was active in 1916. "C" Company of the 227th Battalion, C.E.F., was stationed in Sudbury, with other companies at the Sault, on Manitoulin Island and at Chapleau. Sudburians were chagrined, however, when it was announced that the battalion would winter in Hamilton. They resented the implication that the Sudbury climate was too severe, and there were many uncomplimentary references in the Sudbury papers to the wet, muggy weather at Hamilton as compared with the clear, bracing atmosphere of the north.

With the death of Daniel Baikie, on December 29, 1916, the town lost another link with its early days. A resident for twenty-six years, he had been one of the most active in public enterprises, and was especially interested in education, having served on both the public and high school boards. He had been largely instrumental in the establishment of the high school. His book and stationery business, which a few years before his death he had sold to Frank Muirhead, was one which would have reflected credit on a much larger place than Sudbury.

As the war dragged on through 1916 into 1917, war activities occupied more and more of the people's time and energy. Campaigns were held to raise money for the Patriotic Fund ($43,750 secured). A shower was held, and three hundred pairs of socks were contributed to the men of "C" Company. On March 1, 1917, Sudbury was selected as the mobilization centre for New Ontario, with Lieut.-Col. W. J. Cressey in charge. Captain Irving was paymaster, and the medical board consisted of Lieuts. H. M. Torrington, A.M.C., W. R. Patterson, A.M.C., and W. A. Dale, A.M.C. All men recruited in Algoma, Manitoulin, Nipissing, Timiskaming, Parry Sound and Sudbury districts were to be brought thereafter to the Sudbury mobilization centre to be passed on by the medical board and attested before joining their units.

In spite of the cares which the war imposed upon everyone, the Parks Commission, headed by W. E. Mason, found time to consider two matters of importance. One was the selection of a site for an athletic park. Although criticized for its action in some quarters, the commission recommended the purchase of four acres, part of which was even then being used for the dumping of refuse. This, however, was the genesis of what is now Memorial Park. The other recommendation was that the Council declare a certain part of the lake section a residential area and prohibit the erection of unsightly buildings in that area. This recommendation was accepted and has preserved the lakefront as a place of beauty.

Perhaps more than some other places, especially in Ontario, Sudbury was divided over the conscription issue in 1917. The large *Canadien* population did not take kindly to the idea, and the election in December was fought with unusual bitterness. E. A. Lapierre, a popular commercial traveller, was the Liberal nominee and Charles Harrison, the government nominee. Lapierre had a majority of about 1,700 in the Sudbury district, which, through the provisions of the Wartime Voters Act, was nullified by the soldiers' vote. Lapierre claimed that his local majority was greater than the number of soldiers who had enlisted from the district.

The war had not progressed very far before the importance of nickel became evident, and soon the facilities of both Inco and Mond were strained to the limit to meet the need, their task not made any easier by the diminishing supply of manpower. The end of the war saw production at both plants greatly increased over pre-war levels, and this was to provide problems in the post-war years.

There had from the beginning been an agitation to have the refining of nickel done in Canada, and, as has already been mentioned, the Canadian Copper Company had been authorized to do business in Canada only on that understanding. This had never been insisted upon by the government, and there is no doubt that before Mond undertook his extensive expenditures, which were predicated upon exporting matte to Wales, he had received some assurances that refining in Canada would not be made compulsory.

During the first years of the war, with the United States a neutral country and the greater part of Sudbury's nickel production going to that country for refining, it was an unpleasant thought in Canadian minds that a large part of this nickel could get into the hands of the enemy. This fear was strengthened by the spectacular feat of the German submarine *Deutschland*, which crossed the Atlantic and returned carrying a cargo which included nickel. Thereafter the clamour for the building of a nickel refinery in Canada became more insistent.

On September 9, 1915, the Ontario government appointed a commission, later converted into a Royal Commission, charged with the duty of making a full inquiry into and report upon "the resources, industries, and capacities, both present and future, . . . in connection with nickel and its ores" and upon a "just and equitable system of taxation" of the "mines, minerals and mineral industries," etc.

The Commission consisted of George T. Holloway, of London, England, associate of the Royal College of Sciences and vice-president of the Institution of Mining and Metallurgy, chairman; Willet G. Miller, of Toronto, provincial geologist; McGregor Young, of Toronto, a lawyer; and Thomas W. Gibson, Deputy Minister of Mines of Ontario, secretary.

Stripped of legal verbiage, the commissioners were asked to investigate and report upon the nickel industry in all its phases, in Canada and elsewhere, with full power to summon witnesses and require the production of documents and to take evidence under oath. They were asked to make such recommendations as in their opinion might render the industry of greater value to the province, the dominion and the empire. In addition, they were asked to suggest a just and equitable system of taxation. This had been a contentious subject for some years.

At last, under the stress of war, "Old Nick's" metal had come to be recognized as having an important place in the world's economy.

The investigation and the writing of the report took a year and a half, and in that time a vast amount of information had been gathered and assimilated. Members of the commission had visited most of the nickel-producing countries, and had consulted the leading authorities on various phases of the industry.

The report, dated March 19, 1917, clearly and simply written, is a detailed account of the industry up to the time of writing. The two questions previously agitating the public mind: (1) Can nickel be economically refined in Ontario? and (2) Are the nickel deposits of Ontario of such a character that this province can compete successfully as a nickel producer with any other country? were both answered in the affirmative.

Conclusions were as follows:

1. The nickel ore deposits of Ontario are much more extensive and offer better facilities for the production of nickel at low cost than do those of any other country. Nickel-bearing ores occur in many parts of the world, but the great extent of the deposits in the province, their richness and uniformity in metal contents, and the success of the industry, point strongly to the conclusion that Ontario nickel has little to fear from competition.

2. Any of the processes now in use for the refining of nickel could be successfully worked in Ontario, and conditions and facilities are at least as good in this province as in any other part of Canada.

3. In view of the fact that practically no chemicals are required, that there is a much more complete saving of the precious metals, especially platinum and palladium, and that electric power is cheap and abundant, the most satisfactory method of refining in Ontario will be electrolytic.

4. The refining of nickel in Ontario will not only benefit the nickel industry, but will promote the welfare of existing branches of the chemical and metallurgical industries, and lead to the introduction of others.

5. The methods employed at the Ontario plants of the two operating nickel companies are modern and efficient, although there are differences in both mining and smelting practice. It

is the consistent practice of both companies to adopt all modern improvements in plant and treatment. Even during the present time of acute pressure the Canadian Copper Company has materially increased its output without substantial enlargement of its plant, and the losses in smelting are less both at Copper Cliff and the Mond plant at Coniston than they were a year ago. These companies have had their experimental stage, neither has asked nor received any governmental assistance, and both have earned the success which they have achieved.

6. The present system of taxation in Ontario is just and equitable and in the public interest, and is the best system for this province. Any question of change is rather one of rate than of principle.

Detailed discussion of the investigations leading up to these conclusions follows in fourteen extensive chapters, ending with an appendix containing transcripts of evidence given by many of those who appeared before the commission. The whole constitutes the most comprehensive account of the nickel industry so far written.

One direct result was the decision of the International Nickel Company to build an electrolytic refinery at Port Colborne, Ontario, not far from the entrance to the Welland Canal, at an estimated cost of $4,000,000. As further evidence of the transfer of control over all processes, mining, smelting and refining, to Canada, a subsidiary company called the International Nickel Company of Canada, Limited, was incorporated on July 25, 1916, under Canadian charter. The refinery was completed and put into operation as the war came to a close.

Although promoted and incorporated before the war, the British America Nickel Corporation Limited was largely a product of the war effort. It provides a further chapter in the tragic history of nickel company failures. Its organization was due chiefly to the energy of Dr. F. S. Pearson, a British-American financier, in association with James H. Dunn, a Canadian financier living in London, and E. R. Wood of Toronto.

Previous to the company's incorporation in 1913, these three men had secured options on the properties in the

Sudbury district of the Dominion Nickel-Copper Company Limited and also the rights for North America in the Hybinette refining process. Mining properties involved included the Murray, Gertrude, Elsie, Lady Violet, Whistle, Wildcat, Falconbridge, Blue Ridge, Victor and Nickel Lake.

The outbreak of war rendered financing almost impossible, and the death of Dr. Pearson, who went down with the *Lusitania* in 1915, seemed the final blow, but the company found its opportunity in the concern which developed over the fact that, although producing the bulk of the world's nickel, the British Empire did not have adequate control of its disposal. The British government was induced to assume financial control of the company (securing $14,500,000 of the $20,000,000 capital stock), and to provide an assured market for its product by undertaking to buy a large part of its production.

New orebodies, especially at the Murray, were disclosed by diamond drilling, and the management decided to establish its smelters at that mine. A three-compartment incline shaft was sunk along the footwall to a depth of 1,200 feet, and within a short while from 1,200 to 1,400 tons of ore were being produced daily.

The smelter started with two blast furnaces and basic-lined converters, which were capable of handling 1,000 tons of ore a day. Since the company was determined to have its matte refined in Canada, several sites for the refinery had been considered before the decision was reached to establish it at Deschenes, Quebec, near Ottawa, convenient to both transportation and power. It had an initial capacity of 15,000,000 pounds of nickel, but could be expanded at little additional cost to handle from 20,000,000 to 24,000,000 pounds a year.

The war, with its assured market and relatively high prices, was over before the company got fairly into its stride, and it was forced to suspend operations during the postwar slump. Operations were resumed in 1923, following a reorganization of the company, but within a year the British America Nickel Corporation, Limited, had joined the long list of nickel failures.   On May 15, 1925, its assets were sold under the hammer to a lawyer acting for Inco for $5,000,000, which represented but a few cents per dollar on the money invested in its stocks and bonds.   This company which had seemed to have everything—adequate capital, an assured market, commercial grade ore— apparently lacked that most elusive of all commodities, managerial ability.

Once more the Sudbury field was confined to the two companies which alone seemed to have what it takes—Inco and Mond, soon to join forces, but not for long to enjoy the field in isolation, for another company, till then strange to the nickel industry, would appear to participate in the development of Sudbury Basin.

# XIII

# *New Uses for Nickel*

DURING THE WAR YEARS. BOTH INCO AND Mond had devoted all their energies to meeting the enormous demands made upon them. Since finding new uses for nickel was no longer necessary, their research departments now gave full attention to the production of materials that would as completely as possible meet the insatiable demands of war. Steps were taken to improve mining and metallurgical methods in order to increase production with the least possible additional equipment, and production figures for the war years graphically indicate the manner in which this was achieved.

In 1914, a normal year, 45,517,937 pounds of nickel and 28,948,211 pounds of copper were produced; but during the next four years production steadily increased till, in 1918, 92,507,293 pounds of nickel and 47,074,475 pounds of copper came from Sudbury mines.

While hostilities lasted the war effort had claimed everyone's attention to the exclusion of all else, with little or no thought for the day when there should be no war; and therefore, when the Armistice unexpectedly came and the war ended, the nickel industry was faced with an entirely new set of problems. Few others had so completely been diverted into the channels of war. The nickel industry found itself with mines whose production had been vastly increased, but with practically no markets. Nevertheless, in the hope of a speedy change-over, production had continued through 1919 at a fairly high level, which was considerably increased in 1920; but, instead of the hoped for return of civilian demand, a severe depression set in, catching the nickel companies with heavy inventories against a drastic shrinking in demand. Inco, with its principal market in the United States, was forced to suspend operations for twelve months during 1921 and 1922, while Mond, whose markets were chiefly in Europe, was able to continue, although at a much lower rate of production. Consequently, during the years 1921 and 1922, Sudbury mines produced (1921) 19,293,060 pounds of nickel and 12,821,385 pounds of copper; and (1922) 17,597,123 pounds of nickel and 10,943,636 pounds of copper.

Naturally, it was a time of hardship for miners, and their families, and this was reflected in reduced sales by business firms of all kinds. The Sudbury district was hard hit. In those days, before the lessons of the Great Depression had been learned, no provision existed for public relief, and the unemployed had to shift for themselves as best they could. Many miners left Sudbury for the gold mines of Porcupine and the new ones being opened up at Kirkland Lake. J. A. Laberge was mayor during 1920 and 1921, giving place to Dr. Arthur at the end of the latter year. It was a difficult period for both.

The year 1921 had been a disastrous one for the automotive industry, from which the nickel mines had expected to secure much new business. In that year the production of motor vehicles in the United States declined $700,000,000 from that of the previous year, and this decline was reflected in many other industries.

Although Inco's mines, milling plants and refineries were closed down, its activities increased in other directions. In 1905, Robert C. Stanley, then assistant general superintendent of the Orford Copper Company's Bayonne (N.J.) plant, had first produced "Monel" metal, an alloy of nickel and copper produced direct from the ore without separating the nickel and copper. Many uses had been found for this white metal, but since the percentages of nickel and

ROBERT C. STANLEY         SAMUEL J. RITCHIE

E. A. COLLINS          R. LESLIE BEATTIE

CREIGHTON HEADFRAME COMBINES BEAUTY WITH UTILITY

TWENTY-TON ELECTRIC LOCOMOTIVE AND SECTION OF INCO'S 325 MILES
OF UNDERGROUND WORKINGS

copper are not constant in the ore even from a single mine, it was not practicable to produce Monel in standard mill forms of rod, sheet, strip and wire, and this restricted its field of usefulness.

Inco now decided to develop special uses for Monel, and in 1921 built a refinery and rolling mill at Huntington, West Virginia, to produce it and other alloys. In succeeding years a wide variety of alloys containing nickel were evolved and introduced to markets which the sales and research departments had established for them.

With the election of Stanley to the presidency of Inco in 1922, the company inaugurated an aggressive programme of development, research and sales promotion which, with the return of better times, led to many new uses and markets for nickel. In England, the Mond company was equally active. Due in part to its efforts during the first few years after the war, nine different countries issued new nickel coins. The company also made efforts to stimulate the use of nickel cooking utensils, and this led to the absorption of Henry Wiggin and Company which enabled Mond to enter into the production of nickel and nickel alloys in rolled forms, and of cobalt metal, oxides and salts.

It was at this time also that Mond turned its attention to the recovery of the precious metals—gold, silver, platinum, palladium, ruthenium, rhodium and iridium— contained in the previously discarded residues from the Clydach refinery. A disused soap factory occupying part of the site of the Marshalsea debtors' prison in southeast London was acquired, and here Bernard Mohr set up a pilot plant to conduct researches into the problems connected with the refining of these metals. The success of these experiments led to the establishment of a specially designed full-scale refinery at Acton, which is still employed for the refining of precious metals.

While the nickel companies were thus energetically promoting the use of nickel in every conceivable direction, industry itself went more than half way to meet them.

The greatest single instance of this, of course, was in the automotive industry which, in the postwar years (except for 1921) not only greatly increased the production of cars and trucks, but was more and more concerned with securing materials that were both strong and light. Nickel steels containing from one and one-half per cent to five and one-half per cent nickel were found invaluable for gears, steering parts, crankshafts and other vital parts of motor vehicles.

The increases in the use of heavy machines and equipment such as trucks, buses, tractors, bulldozers, power shovels and freight cars and locomotives made ever greater demands upon the nickel producers. Every extension of industries in which durability of materials coupled with relative lightness was essential made additional calls upon them. In view of the hard usage to which mining equipment is put, it was perhaps not strange that nickel should have entered into the manufacture of a large percentage of it. Rock drills, power shovels, overhead cranes, electric motors and generators, machine tools, mucking machines, mine cars and locomotives, tipples, conveyors, hoists, and a great deal of similar equipment was constructed of alloys in which nickel played a greater or less part.

The airplane industry, just making a beginning in the years following World War I, demanded another type of alloys, those combining lightness, strength and resistance to heat, all of which could be found in nickel alloys; but not until after another world war had been fought would this industry call upon the metallurgists for alloys of still greater tensile strength and resistance to heat.

Since the introduction of Monel, an important market for nickel alloys had been provided by the manufacturers of household utensils, but it remained for the multiplication of electrical household appliances to bring nickel extensively into the home. With the radio, the electric refrigerator, the vacuum cleaner, and dozens of other appliances and utensils, nickel became an indispensable adjunct to modern living. And while the housewife was busy with a stainless steel knife, slicing the ingredients of a salad, her husband might be slicing into the rough with golf clubs the essential part of which had originated in a Sudbury mine.

Thus, beginning in 1923, without benefit of war or fear of war, the nickel industry built itself securely into the world's economy, and by 1928 Sudbury mines produced a record total of 96,755,578 pounds of nickel, exceeded the next year when 110,275,912 pounds were produced. Following that came the depression, when production totals dropped back in 1932 to a low of 30,327,968 pounds of nickel, though the industry was relatively no worse off than any other; in fact, it was less hard hit than some.

# XIV

# *Lindsley Looks into the Basin*

From the time that prospectors first began to comb the Sudbury hills the nickel irruptive has claimed most of the attention of mining men, but it is likely that in future some will be directed toward the silver-copper-lead-zinc deposits now being developed in the interior of the basin itself.

The interior consists of a fairly level post-glacial mantle. Once densely forested, it is now, where soil permits, largely under crop. At present the crop is mostly hay, but some sections are becoming noted for potatoes. It is served by the towns of Chelmsford, Capreol, Larchwood and one or two smaller places. Vermilion River and its chief tributaries, Onaping River and Whitson Creek, drain it toward the southwest, the river expanding into Vermilion Lake, about five miles long, near the southwestern end of the basin.

The rocks in the basin constitute a series unrelated to any others nearby. Beginning with a basal conglomerate, they pass into tuff, slate and sandstone, to which local names have been given. The series has buckled into a basinlike syncline having an inward dip of about thirty degrees. The sandstone (Chelmsford), however, forms a succession of dome-shaped anticlines along the main axis.

The first claims within the basin were staked along Whitson Creek in Balfour township in 1897 by James Stobie, who found mineralized outcrops which he thought might be valuable for sulphur and arsenic.   About the same time a Frenchman named Ollier discovered what proved to be a large silver-lead-copper-zinc deposit on adjoining property, which he staked for himself and partners.   This created considerable interest, which subsided when it became evident that the ore was so complex that no existing method would refine it.   None of the large mining companies could be induced to attempt development; and Ollier, refusing frequent proposals from promoters long on promises and short on cash, tenaciously held on to his property.

Stobie optioned his claims to G. R. Leckie, of the Orford Copper Company, who put down a shaft which, however, did not disclose values sufficient to justify further work.   One of those employed in the shaft-sinking was Joseph Errington, whose destiny was to be closely linked with Sudbury Basin.

Errington was typical of the generation of men who discovered and developed mines along the northern frontier of Canada in the first half of the twentieth century.   Born on an Ontario farm, he had set off at an early age for what was then the frontier outpost of Sudbury.   He had worked for the Canadian Copper Company in various capacities, at the Creighton among other places, and probably because of the close connection between the Canadian Copper Company and the Orford company he was chosen by Leckie to assist in sinking the shaft on the Stobie property.

Leaving Sudbury in 1909, Errington went west to prospect for coal in the Rocky Mountains, after which he worked in mines in the western United States and Mexico. He returned to Ontario in 1923, and became interested in Porcupine gold mines, especially McIntyre-Porcupine, of which he became a director and a considerable shareholder.

It was at this time that Thayer Lindsley, with whom he was to be associated until his death, became acquainted

with him.    Lindsley, who grew up in a suburb of Boston and
was educated at Harvard, had, with his brother Halstead,
become interested in Canadian mining during the early
twenties.   Recognized today as an outstanding mine-
maker, Lindsley at that time (1924) was acting as a roving
geologist for McIntyre, and in this way came frequently
in touch with Errington.   Once, when he had been asked
to report on a prospect in Gowganda, he noted that the
property was part of a basin-like structure, and this
reminded him that the greatest of all geological basins was
at Sudbury, and that rather than waste time at Gowganda
he should be devoting his attention to Sudbury.

In discussions with Errington, the latter told of his early
experiences in Sudbury Basin and suggested that recent
advances in metallurgy might make it possible to treat the
ore on the Ollier claims, still standing idle.   Errington and
Lindsley decided to investigate the possibilities, and Ollier
was at length persuaded to give an option.   Errington
succeeded in interesting the Treadwell-Yukon Mining
Company of San Francisco, controlled by the Bradleys, one
of whom (P. R.) had worked as smelter superintendent for
the Canadian Copper Company while Errington was in its
employ.

Ollier was paid $57,000 in cash for the option and
promptly departed for France.   Errington secured an
interest in the enterprise and became its manager, immediately beginning a programme of diamond drilling along
the northeast-southwest fault zone running parallel to the
slate-tuff contact, to which the mineralization seemed to be
related.

In the meantime, Lindsley and Errington had staked a
large area along Vermilion Lake, immediately to the west,
which the Sudbury Basin Mines Limited was incorporated
to hold and develop.   It was agreed that drilling should be
done on the Sudbury Basin claims to cover assessment
requirements, but when the drill had cut what has been
described as "fantastic" ore, Lindsley discovered that it
was all on the Treadwell side of the line.   He protested,

and a stock adjustment was made by which part of the ground was transferred to Sudbury Basin Mines Limited.

These were boom days in Canada; the public was avid for mining shares, and Sudbury Basin Mines had little difficulty in disposing of its shares at good prices. Treadwell-Yukon was financed by the Bradleys, of course, largely through other companies controlled by them.

Errington sank three shafts (619, 1,572 and 409 feet, respectively) on what came to be known as the Errington mine, where 26,000 feet of lateral work was done on four levels. In April, 1928, a 200-ton pilot plant was installed, and continued in operation until November, 1930. During this time, 164,000 tons of ore were treated, averaging: gold, 0.03 ounces; silver, 1.67 ounces; copper, 1.09 per cent; lead, 1.06 per cent; and zinc, 4.66 per cent. These returns were felt to justify the installation of a 2,000-ton mill, but before this was undertaken the deepening depression and the decline of metal prices forced the suspension of all operations.

Sudbury Basin Mines Limited became a holding company, using its funds to assist in the development of other mining properties, and Lindsley was soon to present it with an opportunity to participate in the flotation of a company destined to become an important factor in the future of Sudbury Basin.

In the meantime there had gathered about Lindsley a group of mining men who were to continue with him as long as they lived. Foremost of these were his brother Halstead and Joe Errington; others were Donald M. Hogarth and C. D. H. MacAlpine. Together they shared in the promotion of Sherritt-Gordon in northwestern Manitoba, and the Beattie in northwestern Quebec, and in order to handle such operations a company called Ventures Limited, of which Thayer Lindsley was president and the others directors, was incorporated in 1928.

Although circumstances had directed the interests of the group elsewhere, Lindsley was still intrigued by the geology of Sudbury Basin, and especially the possibilities of nickel.

But nickel mining at that time was entirely in the hands of Inco and Mond. In Falconbridge township, however, where Thomas A. Edison had unsuccessfully attempted to sink a shaft in 1902-1903, extensive nickel-copper deposits had been discovered by the E. J. Longyear Company of Minneapolis, drilling in 1916-1917.

In 1915 William E. Smith, formerly of Minneapolis, a lawyer-turned-prospector, became imbued with the possibilities of the one-time Edison holdings which by then had reverted to the Crown. Through Hugh Roberts, a well-known geologist, he secured the backing of the Minneapolis and Michigan Development Company of Minneapolis for whom he staked the property. The company, of which R. M. Bennett was president and the E. J. Longyear Company, mining engineers of Minneapolis, managers, later transferred its interest in the claims to a Canadian company incorporated for the purpose, Falconbridge Mines Limited.

This property seemed most promising to Lindsley and, in the summer of 1928 he commissioned Robert Hoffman, a Boston mining engineer, well known in Canadian mining, to go to Minneapolis on his behalf and sound out the Longyear-Bennett interests. Hoffman returned with the information that a deal could be made. Then, accompanied by J. Gordon Hardy, a Scottish engineer (though born in Chile) until recently employed by the American Smelting & Refining Company, Lindsley went to Minneapolis to continue the negotiations. An agreement was soon reached under which Falconbridge Mines Limited agreed to sell its properties for $2,500,000, of which $500,000 was to be cash, the balance to be paid within a few months. Shortly after, the participants, with their lawyers and engineers, met in Toronto to complete the deal.

Falconbridge Nickel Mines Limited was incorporated by the Lindsley group on August 28, 1928, and the properties were at once transferred to it, Ventures receiving stock in the new company for its cash advances. Ventures invested an additional $250,000 and Sudbury Basin Mines Limited also helped in the financing (on December 31, 1930, Sudbury Basin Mines Limited held thirty-nine per cent of Falconbridge's issued shares).

Although the price was the highest ever paid for any mine in Sudbury district, the purchasers took no chances. The price was based on engineers' estimates of 5,700,000 tons of ore above the 500-foot level, upon which a value of fifty cents a ton was placed, and the transaction has been fully justified by subsequent events.

With Gordon Hardy as consulting engineer and Ernest Craig as mine manager, Falconbridge Nickel Mines Limited lost no time in proceeding to make a mine. A new shaft, 100 feet west of Edison's, was sunk 1,000 feet, with levels opened at 225, 350 and 1,000 feet.

One of the first steps taken, in addition to shaft-sinking and the provision of mine buildings and living quarters, was to protect the company's holdings by the staking of adjoining territory, thus early putting into effect a policy which eventually was to ensure the company's expansion far beyond anything then anticipated.

When work began in the fall of 1928 only a wood road connected the mine with the nearest small settlement at Garson, three miles away. By the spring of 1930 the shaft was down and a smelter had been built, ready to treat upward of three hundred tons of ore a day; railway connection had been secured; a modern townsite with adequate water supply and sewage disposal works had been provided, with accommodation for five hundred people and a school for sixty pupils.

In the interval, Gordon Hardy had gone to Norway to acquire the Kristiansand refinery which owned the rights on the Hybinette refining process, after which Anton Gronningsater, for many years with Inco at Copper Cliff, who had transferred to the first Falconbridge company in 1927 and to the new one on its formation, was sent to Norway to modernize this refinery and increase its capacity.

The refinery, operated under a wholly-owned subsidiary called Falconbridge Nikkelverk Aktieselskap, was in charge of S. B. Steen, local manager.

Thus another nickel company had come to share the field with Inco and Mond, a company that would not fail as its numerous predecessors had done, but which, with the passing years, would become a powerful factor in the affairs of Sudbury district. With the amalgamation of Inco and Mond in 1929, the nickel industry would again revert to two great companies.

# XV

# *Inco and Mond Unite*

For more than a quarter century Inco and Mond had controlled the world's nickel industry. They existed side by side, yet their interests had clashed very little. Regardless of the other, each had gone its way.

Inco's milling, smelting and administrative centre was at Copper Cliff, four miles west of Sudbury. Although it owned many mines along the south rim of the basin, during most of the time since Mond's arrival at the turn of the century its ore had been drawn chiefly from the Creighton, some seven miles west of Copper Cliff.

Mond's smelting centre was at Coniston, about eight miles southeast of Sudbury, and its ore supply came mostly from the Garson mine about four miles north of Coniston, but also from the Levack, the only producing mine on the north rim, thirty miles away.

Inco's refinery was at Port Colborne, Ontario, and its markets were chiefly in the United States; while Mond's refinery was at Clydach, Wales, and its markets were almost entirely European.

The two companies might have continued in this way indefinitely but for a circumstance which neither had anticipated and which had not previously been apparent. The great Frood deposit was discovered by Thomas Frood and James Cockburn in 1884 on lots 6 and 7 in the sixth concession of McKim township. Lot 6 was allotted to

141

Cockburn and lot 7 to Frood. Cockburn sold his claim to the Canadian Copper Company, and Frood did likewise with respect to the south half of lot 7, but did not apply for the north half. This, later called the Frood Extension, was later staked by William McVittie in association with Frank Cochrane who, in 1911, sold it to the Mond company.

Except for stripping and trenching, no work was done on either property until 1899, when the Canadian Copper Company started open-pit mining, with shipments to Copper Cliff in 1900 when a railway spur was extended to the mine. Shipments were discontinued in 1903, after a total of 107,942 tons of ore averaging 2.66 per cent nickel and 1.39 per cent copper had been taken out.

In 1913 and 1914, in anticipation of an early exhaustion of Creighton ore, Inco had made preparations to re-open the Frood. A townsite was laid out and a water system installed. Before the shift was made, however, drilling disclosed large orebodies at the Creighton, and development at the Frood was again suspended.

At about the same time the Mond company decided to develop the Frood Extension; but after sinking a shaft to a depth of 1,000 feet, work was stopped without production having been reached, probably because of the unexpected extent of the Levack deposit and the richness of its ore (nickel 3.2 per cent, copper 1.15 per cent).

When the depression of the early twenties had passed and new uses had been found for nickel, Inco again decided to open the Frood, beginning work in September, 1926, on its No. 3 shaft, completed to a depth of 3,045 feet on March 27, 1928. The Mond company was also proceeding with development, deepening its shaft, first to 2,000 feet, and later to 3,000 feet.

In the meantime, drilling had established the Frood deposit as the greatest in the Sudbury field, and it became evident that Inco and Mond were owners of different parts of a single deposit. If development were to continue independently, two complete sets of everything would be required, and the best solution seemed that either should sell its interest to the other, but this neither cared to do. The only alternative was for the two companies to amalgamate, and, as it happened, the different characteristics of the two groups made this possible.

It will be remembered that the Mond company had originally been a chemical concern, headed by men of a scientific bent of mind, but shrewd men of business as well. The invention of a nickel refining process had been more or less an accident, and Ludwig Mond was quite prepared to sell it if he could have found a purchaser, but having failed, and in order to capitalize on his invention, he was drawn across the Atlantic into the difficult field of nickel mining.

Men who follow mining by preference usually have a streak of the gambler in their makeup; the most successful ones are careful to avail themselves of all the knowledge and skills available, but they still count also upon "getting the breaks." The Ritchies and Thompsons, ancestors of Inco, were men of that stamp. They were in business to make money, of course, but they also derived from their operations the other kind of satisfaction which men of this type experience in their work.

There had been many more failures than successes in the nickel industry. The Vivians, despite their long experience in metals, had failed in their attempt, and many other companies, for one reason or another, were to succumb. Not the least of these was the British America Nickel Corporation, with the British government as a financial backer.

The Monds had succeeded; yet, in the three decades since their entry into Canada, they had changed their ways very little. They had remained essentially a British organization. Ludwig's eldest son, who now headed the company, had become a distinguished figure in British public life and in 1910 had been made a baronet. Elevated to the House of Lords as Lord Melchett in 1928, he was prominent in international finance. The family, while proud of its success in the nickel industry, were not at all sentimental about it; they were quite capable of assessing its value in cold cash without requiring a bonus to salve the pain of severed sentimental ties.

On the other hand, Inco was controlled by men who had grown up in the nickel industry, with no other major interests. Typical of these was Robert C. Stanley, now its president, who had been with the company and its predecessors since 1901 and by now was considered one of the outstanding leaders of industry in the United States. First and foremost he was a metallurgist, but he also had a wide understanding of the function of a large enterprise in the modern economic world; and he and his associates had the North American point of view, which is always more or less tinged with optimism, hopeful of bigger and better things to come.

It was therefore quite natural that Inco should be prepared to absorb the Mond company, and equally natural that the latter should be content with such an outcome. As shrewd financiers with more than a quarter of a century's experience in the nickel business, the Monds knew that by exchanging Mond shares for shares in International Nickel they could not lose. The transaction was easily and quickly settled. It was not a case of the larger corporation dominating the lesser one; it was a mutually satisfactory arrangement which neither party has ever had any reason to regret.

Inco's board of directors was increased to include Mond representatives, chief of whom were Lord Melchett, his son Henry and his brother Robert, besides J. P. Bickell, of Toronto, then president of McIntyre-Porcupine, as well as others in the United Kingdom and the United States.

In 1902, when the International Nickel Company was organized, production of nickel from Sudbury ores amounted to 10,693,410 pounds. By 1929, when Inco and Mond joined, production had increased to 110,275,912 pounds, an all-time record. World consumption stood at 120,000,000 pounds, and prospects seemed good for a steady increase. None could then see the depression lurking round the corner. The nickel industry, however, was one of the first to recover (production in 1934 exceeded that of 1929 by 25,000,000 pounds).

Until a short while before the merger, Inco's ore supply was still derived entirely from the Creighton, mostly from the open pit, which eventually became 200 feet deep, 670 feet long and 180 feet wide. At first, ore was removed by derricks, but when the pit got too deep for this method, shafts were sunk in the footwall adjoining the pit, which was connected to the shaft by drives at different levels. The ore was trammed to the shaft and hoisted to the surface in the usual way.

When all the ore that could be safely recovered had been obtained, the shafts were deepened and ore secured from underground by overhand stopings. One of the earliest forms of stoping was what is called shrinkage mining which consisted of removing just enough ore after each stope-cut was broken down to provide room for miners to work standing on top of it, consideration being given to the fact that broken ore occupies about forty per cent more space than solid rock. The miners then drilled out another seven-foot slice above them, which when broken down by blasting (and after the usual proportion had been removed) provided a base for the next stope, and so on, until all the ore in a given section was ready for removal. While one set of miners were working in this manner, another set, by driving crosscuts and drifts, were preparing other levels from which the miners could work and by which the ore would be removed.

It was usually necessary to leave pillars of ore to prevent caving, which resulted in the loss of much good ore; consequently, about the time of the merger, methods were adopted to make more complete ore recovery possible. In one of these, called cut-and-fill, areas mined out were filled with sand, gravel or crushed rock. Square-set mining is a variation of this process. To prevent caving, stopes were fitted with timber frames consisting of posts and horizontal pieces, each so fashioned as to form a compact square. As

mining proceeded, these were built alongside and on top of
each other, like cells in a honeycomb, and they too were
usually filled with waste material.

Later, when large bodies of lower grade ore were mined,
other methods were adopted, which will be described in
later chapters.

Following quickly upon the merger came the construction at Copper Cliff of an 8,000-tons-per-day flotation mill,
the result of previous experiments in selective flotation by
both Mond and Inco. This process consists in putting
previously crushed (one-quarter inch or less) ore through a
grinding mill which reduces it to powder. The first sixteen
grinding mills (Marcy) were in operation at Copper Cliff
by August, 1930. These mills, six and one-half feet by
twelve feet, electrically driven, partly filled with two-and-
one-half-inch steel rods and partly filled with crushed ore
mixed with water, rotated on a horizontal axis and in the
process pounded the ore to a powder which, because of the
water, had the consistency of porridge.

The mixture of powdered ore and water next passed to
the flotation cells, a series of shallow tanks, seventy-two of
which were twenty feet long and sixty-eight, twelve feet
long, through which it was kept in movement by revolving
paddles. Further water was added as well as certain oily
chemicals. Air forced through the moving mass from below
caused the chemicals to form a thick froth of bubbles on
the surface of the water. The bubbles picked up the
sulphides, allowing the rocky material to drop to the
bottom, while the oily scum, with the sulphides, was
skimmed off the top.

In other tanks, the copper sulphides were floated off
and the nickel sulphides settled to the bottom. Thus the
two metals, fused by the forces of nature so that they stick
closer than brothers, are finally separated. The nickel,
plus some copper and other impurities, is shipped to the
nickel refinery at Port Colborne.

With the bulk of millfeed coming from the flotation
plant, a change was necessary at the smelting end, and the

Frood-Stobie Open Pit

Inco Smelter, Copper Cliff

first reverberatory furnaces (five) were installed. In these furnaces the flame is above the contents, air is not forced through from below as in the case of blast furnaces, but is introduced through apertures (tuyeres) higher up. In addition, six roasters and eight basic lined converters were provided to reduce the proportion of sulphur.

Thus the first stage in the establishment of a fully modern plant was reached; and, with modifications, the processes installed in 1930 were to continue in use for the next twenty years, except for increases in capacity.

Another advance at Copper Cliff was the completion in 1930 of an electrolytic copper refinery with a rated capacity of 20,000,000 pounds of copper a month. This plant was built by the Ontario Refining Company, Limited, an Inco subsidiary, on a sixty-acre site approximately one and one-quarter miles southwest of the Copper Cliff smelter, with which it was connected by standard gauge railway. At first the blister copper was shipped from the smelter to the refinery in 450-pound pigs, but after a few years it was shipped in molten condition in cars specially constructed of steel plate lined with magnesite refractories backed by fire brick.

From the cars the copper is dumped into the anode furnaces, where a preliminary refining occurs, and then the molten metal goes to the thirty-six-foot casting wheel where twenty-two slabs, thirty-six inches square and one and one-half inches thick, weighing 580 pounds, are cast.

In the next process, these anodes, consisting of copper, plus various impurities, are immersed in deposition tanks filled with a solution of copper sulphates, where they remain for four weeks. During that time the anodes are dissolved by the solution, the impurities drop to the bottom, and the pure copper (99.97 per cent) is re-deposited in the form of cathodes. The latter, when melted, are cast into the many shapes needed in industry.

Improvements were also made at Clydach, the most important of which was provision for the replacement of bessemer matte from Coniston by material from Port

Colborne containing much less copper and a much higher percentage of nickel. With increasing production of nickel and copper, the production of precious metals was also increased, and this made necessary an enlargement of the Acton refinery and an improvement in the processes involved. The Acton plant thus became the largest producer of platinum metals in the world.

At the Mond research laboratory in Birmingham a group of workers undertook researches with the long-term objective of increasing nickel consumption. They advised and co-operated with outside scientific bodies in dealing with problems which might arise in connection with the use or production of nickel alloys. Another section of the research department collected information on nickel from all sources, thus building up what has been described as the most comprehensive metal bibliography ever compiled.

One of the most far-reaching changes instituted by Inco at this time was the establishment of a department of geology. Previous to this there had been one or two geologists on the staff, working under the supervision of the mining engineering department. This move was a reflection of a trend in the United States where, in order to determine depletion rates for taxation and other purposes, accurate estimates of ore possibilities had been found necessary. The taxation problem did not exist in Canada, but from a planning and accounting standpoint it was quite as essential that mines should be able to establish as completely as possible the extent of their ore resources. Not only that, but mining without complete geological data was like working in the dark.

The recognized leader in this movement was L. C. Graton, Professor of Economic Geology at Harvard, who had been retained as consultant by a number of large copper mining companies in the western United States, in Mexico and in South America. In 1930 Graton was retained by Inco, and immediately set up a department of geology at Copper Cliff, headed by A. B. Yates, with a staff of

young geologists, most of whom had done their graduate
work under his direction at Harvard. Among these was
Horace J. Fraser, a young Canadian with a brilliant
scholastic record. He was to remain with Inco until 1935
when he would leave to take a post at the California
Institute of Technology, but this would by no means be
the end of his connection with Sudbury.

The depression had struck before these changes were
completed, and although operations were not suspended,
as in 1921-1922, production for two or three years was
drastically curtailed and the Coniston smelter was shut
down for a few months. A great change had occurred,
however, in the thinking of the men at the head of the
nickel industry as compared with the early twenties.
They now knew that nickel had become an essential factor
in the industrial economy, and that as soon as the depression
was over demand would increase at a faster pace than
ever before. Plans were laid accordingly.

Despite the already wide use of nickel, efforts were
concentrated upon developing still other fields of usefulness,
and new ones stemmed from each fresh discovery. One of
the greatest advances during this period was in the extension of the use of stainless steel (nickel, two to twenty-six
per cent, plus chromium and iron). Steels containing
eight per cent nickel and eighteen per cent chromium were
found to be ideal for utensils in hotel and restaurant
kitchens, and the company's sales department exploited
to the full the opportunity thus presented.

Not only were stainless steels of use in kitchens, but
owing to their resistance to corrosion from fruit and
vegetable juices they made a strong appeal to food pro-
cessers. While the materials displaced were often cheaper,
the longer life of nickel alloys more than made up for the
difference in first cost.

Nickel steel had long been a top requirement in motor
cars, trucks and airplanes, where great strength combined
with lightness was a requisite, but now whole trains were

being built of stainless steel, and the streamliners zooming along many United States railroads bore their share of tribute to the growing importance of nickel.

For some purposes alloys are needed which will not shrink or expand with changes of temperature, while in other cases, such as for thermostats, metals are required that will expand and contract a great deal. In both respects, nickel alloys of different sorts were found to be effective.

In one of its publications, Inco charted the manner in which nickel serves the average person from morning till night, an illuminating illustration of the manner in which this metal, once a nuisance and then a novelty, has won such an indispensable place in people's daily lives.

When at length the depression had lifted, the nickel industry was geared to meet demands little dreamed of even a few years before.

# XVI

# *Depression Days*

SUDBURY HAD EMERGED FROM THE DEPRES-
sion of the early twenties. Mines operated
at full capacity and miners had money in their pockets.
Business was good with the merchants. In 1928 nickel
production topped that of 1927 by thirty million pounds,
and in 1929 it reached an all-time high. The Wall Street
market crash in November, 1929, affected Sudbury scarcely
at all. As 1930 advanced, although the depression was
definitely darkening in other places, Sudbury was still
largely unaffected. Falconbridge blew in its first smelter
in that year and Sudbury's nickel production was only
slightly below the previous year's peak.

By this time the population had increased to over
twenty thousand. Sudbury people were proud of their
community, by far the largest and fastest-growing in
northern Ontario, and would be satisfied with nothing less
than incorporation as a city. Charles McCrea, still their
representative in the legislature and a member of the
government, saw to the passing of the necessary act of
incorporation, and the town became a city.

Few remained of those who, thirty-seven years before,
were citizens of the newly-incorporated town of Sudbury.
Stephen Fournier, the first mayor, after serving for more
than a score of years as registrar of deeds and titles, had
died but a year previously. But P. S. Frawley, the first
town clerk, although not so spry as formerly, was still quite

151

active.  Dr. Howey had failed by a short time to survive until the city's incorporation.  Of the early prospectors, William McVittie, turned eighty in 1930, was one of the few still alive, and he had three years still ahead of him.  That year was a memorable one for McVittie because it marked the culmination of a project (Wahnapitae Power Company) begun by him nearly thirty years before for which he would receive in final settlement a cheque for $1,030,000.  W. J. Bell, the oldest remaining representative of the early lumber barons, was seventy-two in 1930.  He still had many years before him, and his name was already perpetuated by the transfer to the city of land at Lake Ramsay comprised in beautiful Bell Park.

Dr. W. J. Cook, who had become medical officer of health in 1911, still held that position and would continue to do so until his death in 1944, when his son, Dr. J. B. Cook, would succeed him, constituting a remarkable example of father-and-son devotion to public welfare.

Although not one who had come to Sudbury in its village days, John J. Mackey had been a citizen since 1907 when he had come to build a brewery.  In the interval he had been interested in numerous projects, usually concerned with construction of some sort,  and in 1926 had topped his ambition by erecting the five-storey Mackey block on lots at the northeast corner of Durham and Elm, secured as the result of a deal with Foster Shields.

In 1930 Mackey and a group of associates (J. A. Laberge, W. J. Laforest and J. N. Demarais) decided to give the Sudbury *Star* some competition.  They organized the Sudbury Citizen Publishing Company Limited with the intention of producing a daily newspaper, but when the Canadian Press refused them a news service they gave up the idea.

Peter Fenton, who had been active in bringing about the incorporation, was the first mayor of the city of Sudbury. His council consisted of J. W. Brownlee, Fred Davidson, J. B. Ducharme, F. C. Muirhead, James Newburn and L. J. Robert.  W. J. Ross was city clerk, R. H. Grant, treasurer, and G. E. Buchanan, a citizen of Sudbury since 1901, and probably the town's leading lawyer, was city solicitor.

On Friday, August 1, 1930, Sudbury became a city. A "monster" celebration was held the following Monday, which was civic holiday. A "mammoth" parade headed by the bugle band of the 97th Algonquin Regiment, followed by the Algoma company of that regiment, got under way at 1.30 p.m. Decorated floats representing business firms, fraternal organizations, service clubs and various national groups and associations wound in procession along the principal business streets to the music of five other bands stationed at strategic points.

Mayor Fenton, supported on the platform by all the available ex-mayors, delivered the inaugural address. Speeches were also made, among others, by Charles McCrea and William Finlayson, a member of the cabinet specially representing the provincial government.

Adjoining municipalities extended good wishes through their reeves or mayors. The most outstanding of these was easily E. A. Collins, mayor of Copper Cliff and assistant to the vice-president of the International Nickel Company of Canada, Limited. Born on a farm near Smithfield, Ontario, and a graduate of Queen's University, he had come to Copper Cliff in 1918 as Inco's first safety engineer, and through his many public activities had attained a leading position in the Sudbury district, which he would enhance with the passing years until his death in 1952.

In celebration of the event, the *Star*, not yet a daily, brought out a special edition of sixty-four pages, proudly reviewing past progress and confidently predicting greater glories to come. The business people and mining companies showed their appreciation by the liberal purchase of advertising space. W. E. Mason, the *Star's* owner, had become Sudbury's outstanding citizen. After the *Star's* initial failure in 1909, Mason had assumed its management, at first producing it semi-weekly and later three times a week, and eventually welded it into an instrument of power which he used to advance the welfare of Sudbury as he saw it.

Despite the dark clouds which already enveloped a large part of the world's economy, Sudbury celebrated its attainment of city status with much more confidence in the future than was warranted by the portents.  For this there was, however, some justification.  The year 1930 saw the opening of Inco's new concentrator and smelter and the Ontario Refining Company's electrolytic refinery at Copper Cliff as well as the plant of Canadian Industries Limited for the manufacture of nitre cake and sulphuric acid.  The total estimated value of new buildings in Sudbury amounted in that year to $1,904,000, while the assessed value of property within the city reached a total of $12,386,147, evidently on a very conservative basis considering that nearly one-sixth of that amount was represented by buildings constructed or in course of construction during the year.

Yet Sudbury could not indefinitely remain unaffected by the miasma spreading throughout the world.  Nickel markets were shrinking, which soon would be reflected in curtailment of mining activities and the laying-off of men. In June, 1932, the United States congress imposed a duty of four cents per pound on foreign copper, and on December 6th, of the same year, domestic copper sold in the United States at five cents per pound, Connecticut, an all-time low.  During this time Inco was drawing its millfeed from the Frood; the Creighton, Garson and Levack having been closed down.  The Creighton was reopened in 1933, but the Garson and Levack did not reopen till 1936 and 1937, respectively.

With copper, lead and zinc at bed-rock prices, the high hopes so recently held for large-scale operations at the Treadwell-Yukon mine inside the Basin were blasted, and soon all underground work ceased and the plant was shut down. Services were discontinued in the newly-built townsite and those who had come there so hopefully moved away, most of them to Sudbury.

Sudbury has no mines within its limits, and therefore receives no direct revenue from mining. Most of the miners and their families, however, lived either in the city or were dependent upon it. Nearly everyone believed that the depression would be temporary and no provision had been made for the relief of workers whose pay was cut off. Merchants extended credit until their own became impaired and then were forced to insist on cash.

Previous to the depression it was not considered a matter of public concern whether men and women starved. That sort of thing was left to charitable agencies to deal with. But these, swamped with appeals, were soon unable to cope with demands made upon them. Few cities had made any provision, either in cash or personnel, for dealing with such an emergency. Sudbury, no different from other communities, had no relief department and made shift in one way or another to meet the needs of the most urgent cases. When every other resource had failed, Frank Rothery, the sanitary inspector, took the case in hand and averted actual starvation or privation from exposure.

In 1932, however, this procedure, inadequate from the start, was found to be unsatisfactory and a welfare department was organized with S. C. Manson as administrator, a large part of the cost being provided by the provincial government. The newly-organized department, from administrator downward, was untrained and poorly equipped to deal with what was really a major operation in social rehabilitation. Many needy cases were overlooked while others, perhaps more insistent in their demands, received a disproportionate share of attention. The unemployed were perhaps fortunate in having Mrs. A. Charbonneau, later relief administrator herself, in charge of supervision, but at best the relief which could be given often fell far short of what was required for the maintenance of decent self-respect.

With depression general, nothing was to be gained by going somewhere else, but Sudbury contained many whose roots were not very deep and some of these left the city.

This exodus was increased by the departure of those who for some time past had been engaged upon Inco's various construction projects. Consequently, by 1933 the population had dropped from a high of slightly over 20,000 in 1930 to a low of 17,246. In 1932 the total production of nickel had been 30,327,968 pounds, seven million pounds less than had been produced in 1910, representing a drop exceeded only in the dark days of 1921-1922.

The rise of Hitler caused a sharp upturn in the demand for nickel, resulting in production of 83,264,658 pounds in 1933 and 128,687,340 pounds in 1934, with a rapidly ascending scale of production thereafter. This, however, was not immediately reflected in Sudbury's fortune. By now a large portion of the population seemed permanently unemployed, requiring as their destitution deepened increasing sums for direct relief which, in 1936, reached a high of $112,828.48. Although grants from the provincial treasury in the same year amounted to $85,252.54, the drain on the city's resources, with its revenues depleted by unpaid taxes, was more than the corporation could bear. In 1934 Sudbury was forced to default on its bonds, and for the next six years remained under the supervision of the Ontario Department of Municipal Affairs.

Sudbury had attained city status but it still lacked many of the amenities of city life. Among other things it was still without an adequate library. Except for the Copper Cliff hospital, St. Joseph's, founded in 1896 by the Grey Nuns of the Cross, was the only hospital to serve the needs of the 35,000 people in and around Sudbury, to say nothing of those coming from points at a distance.

But perhaps Sudbury's experience in establishing a Y.M.C.A. is more typical of this lack of amenities. Many attempts had been made but Sudbury had become a city without having acquired a Y.M.C.A., and quite possibly was the only place of its size in Canada without such an institution. Several reasons have been advanced, chief of which is the existence of national groups which tend to keep their members segregated and provide services which, if not similar to those supplied by the Y.M.C.A., are at least a substitute. Yet, if members of these organizations were excluded, there should still have been enough un-attached young men to support a Y.M.C.A. But even after it was organized in 1935 its existence was precarious for many years.

Although no one had yet had the temerity to suggest that some day the Canadian Shield might play an important part in determining the cultural climate of Canada, Sudbury, at this time, could scarcely have been submitted as evidence in support of any such thesis.

# XVII

## *Success Story*

IN MINING GENERALLY, AND IN NICKEL MINING particularly, it can be said that success is the exception rather than the rule. This has been amply demonstrated by the history of mining in the Sudbury Basin. Company after company had been hopefully launched, a number with apparently excellent prospects, yet all but two had failed up to the time of the incorporation of Falconbridge Nickel Mines Limited. So when this group of mining promoters, as they seemed, not one with a mine to his credit and none with experience in the highly-specialized field of nickel mining, undertook to develop the property that had beaten the wizard Edison, the betting odds were decidedly against them.

In years to come, Lindsley, Errington, Hogarth, MacAlpine, would become historic names in Canadian mining, names to conjure with; but at that time there was nothing to suggest that they were likely to succeed where the Vivians, the Dominion Nickel-Copper Company, the Lake Superior Power Company and the British America Nickel Corporation had all come to grief. What did these new adventurers have that their predecessors did not have?

Well, they had Thayer Lindsley, for one thing. He firmly believed Sudbury Basin to be one of the most, if not the most remarkable geological structures in the world. He was certain that in time many important new mines would be developed along its rim—as well as within its oval—and he was determined to make Falconbridge Nickel Mines Limited the chief agency and forerunner of these future mines. Consequently, no sooner had the company been incorporated and started on its way than, through the Sudbury Nickel and Copper Company Limited, an associated company, he began acquiring properties wherever possible along the rim, aggregating within the first year many thousands of acres besides the 7,960 acres held by the Falconbridge company itself.

Lindsley, as president of Falconbridge, was ably supported by J. Gordon Hardy, vice-president and consulting engineer. A shrewd and capable mining engineer, Hardy was a good foil for his sometimes overly-optimistic chief. While far-sighted and tenacious when once a course of action was adopted, he was abundantly endowed with Scottish caution, and his other Scottish characteristic, thriftiness, was an added advantage to the company, although often a source of exasperation to those who worked with him.

As mine superintendent, in actual charge of operations at the mine, Lindsley had chosen Ernest Craig, a practical miner, whose experience had been gained principally in northern Ontario and northwestern Quebec and who had a reputation for getting things done. During the previous year he had been in charge of the Aldermac mine in Quebec, operated by Noranda Mines Limited.

Halstead Lindsley, brother of Thayer and a close associate, was also a vice-president. Norman F. Parkinson, secretary of Ventures Limited, was secretary-treasurer, and W. S. Morlock, solicitor for both Ventures and Falconbridge, was the fifth member of the board of directors.

In charge of metallurgical processes as consulting metallurgist, was Anton Gronningsater, who, it will be remembered, had returned to Norway in 1909 to take charge of the Kristiansand refinery, had come back to Canada in 1919 as metallurgist for the British America Nickel Corporation, and after the failure of that company had been engaged by the Bennett-Longyear interests, then owners of the Falconbridge property.   When the latter was acquired by Falconbridge Nickel Mines Limited, Gronning-sater had merely changed employers.

In addition to acreage the new company seemed well supplied with money.  Organized during the boom days preceding the market crash of November, 1929, it had been successful in the sale of its shares.   In his first annual report, at the end of 1929, the company's first full year of operations, Thayer Lindsley was able to report cash on hand, and accruing from stock subscriptions, amounting to $2,358,066.19, with outstanding accounts of only $130,299.85.  Unless further financing were resorted to, this money must, of course, suffice to put the mine into production.

The main Falconbridge property was not unproven ground.  It straddled the strike of the norite-sedimentary contact for a distance of 16,570 feet, 10,420 feet of which comprised an ore zone established by the drilling of the E. J. Longyear Company, estimated to contain 5,700,000 tons of ore above the 500-foot level over a distance of 7,500 feet, the longest continuous stretch of ore yet discovered in Sudbury Basin.

Thus the new project had at least two essentials, money and ore.  Lindsley had not neglected another equally essential one.  Several of the nickel companies that had previously failed had done so because of the lack of refining facilities.  Without a means of refining its matte, a nickel company was practically doomed to failure.  Lindsley had guarded against this contingency immediately after the property had been secured by sending Hardy to Norway to buy the Kristiansand refinery.  Its capacity was inadequate and it was badly in need of repair, so Gronningsater went across to enlarge it and bring it up to the highest point of efficiency.  Having acquired the rights in the Hybinette process, the company would be in a position to control its product from mine to market.  Experience had con-clusively demonstrated that in no other way could a nickel company be sure of success.

It might seem that having a refinery in Norway would be rather unsatisfactory for a mine at Sudbury, but the Mond Nickel Company had successfully shipped its matte across the ocean for thirty years, and Falconbridge undoubtedly could do the same. The European market was expanding and, for the time being at least, Falconbridge was content to seek its markets on that side of the Atlantic. Consequently, after securing the refinery, Hardy arranged with Brandeis, Goldschmidt and Company, London metal dealers, to act as sales agents for the company, an arrangement that worked out very satisfactorily. Thus was the chain complete.

No time was lost. The option agreement had been signed on August 20, 1928, and by September 7th, Craig had a crew on the ground, making preparations for the sinking of a shaft. But first the exact boundaries of the property must be determined. A dozen years had passed since the ground was staked, fires had swept through the country, and in places a dense crop of bushes and small trees had sprung up. Craig hired J. R. Gill, a young civil engineer, son of J. S. Gill, jeweller and former mayor of Sudbury, to run new lines. Shortly after, Gill returned to Falconbridge as smelter superintendent, eventually becoming assistant mine manager.

That year was an active one in Canada, with employment at the full, and consequently the assembling of a competent crew of miners was not the least of Craig's problems. In his difficulty he called on a number of Nova Scotians of Scottish descent and others who had worked for him on previous jobs. Among these was William Light, from Aldermac, and Martin Chesser and Malcolm MacDonald, who came from Kirkland Lake. Far from being deterred by the hardships of opening up a new mine in the bush, these men were intrigued by the prospect and lost no time getting to Falconbridge. Many of them were to remain there and they have played no little part in the mine's successful development.

Watkin Samuel was the first mining engineer, remaining from 1928 to 1931.   In October, 1929, R. M. Oliver arrived to act as his assistant.

Sinking of a three-compartment shaft was begun on September 17th with a crew of twenty-one men, and by the end of thirty days it had reached a depth of 253 feet.   The expected tussle with the quicksand that had stopped Edison did not occur; bedrock was reached at sixty feet without any quicksand having been encountered.   It was then realized how fortunate had been the choice of the shaftsite which happened to be over a point where the rock rose much closer to the surface than only a few yards farther east. The Edison shaft at this point had encountered quicksand at eighty feet.   Continuing into the rock, Craig's crew bottomed the shaft at 1,033 feet, cutting stations at the 225-, 350- and 1,000-foot levels.   The shaft was in the footwall, south of the orebody, and crosscuts were driven north into the latter from which to begin development work.

At first the men were housed in tents, but by the end of the first year, in addition to mine buildings and equipment, accommodation had been provided for 225 men and twenty-five five-room cottages had been erected for men with families.

The original woods road from Garson, three and a half miles to the west, had been improved to carry heavy trucks, and work was progressing on a spur of the Canadian National Railways, opened for service in the following October.

The smeltersite was located on the shore of a small lake about two thousand feet southeast of the shaft.   The smelter layout had been designed by Gronningsater, unfortunately detained himself in Norway, where he was supervising the renovation of the refinery.   Work began on the smelter early in 1929, and by the end of the year the blast furnace, converters and other equipment were practically ready for the beginning of operations scheduled for early in 1930.

Anton Gronningsater

Ernest Craig

C. B. Steen

R. C. Mott

RIX STREET, FALCONBRIDGE

FALCONBRIDGE TOWNSITE

Building the smelter had not been an easy matter for Craig and his crew, none of whom had had much experience in that regard. Craig had seen other smelters erected, and Gill had worked at the Murray mine for the British North America Nickel Corporation while its smelter was being constructed, but that was the extent of their experience. Craig tried unsuccessfully to borrow expert smeltermen from Inco and elsewhere. The reputation that had been given Falconbridge by those sceptical of its success and by others even less well-disposed was effective in preventing his getting the assistance he required. Contemptuous remarks were made about the nickel mine being run by a gold miner and a land surveyor. Eventually he succeeded in borrowing a man from Teck-Hughes Gold Mines Limited at Kirkland Lake, with whose help the work proceeded.

During the first year development work was done on the 225- and 1,000-foot levels, and diamond drilling was done from the surface to check the Longyear drilling and from the 1,000-foot level to determine the nature of the orebody at lower depths. While the extent of the orebody did not in every respect equal the Longyear estimates, the grade was better, giving an average of 2.97 per cent nickel and 0.97 per cent copper, which indicated a return at prevailing metal prices of $21.90 per ton.

Meanwhile the depression had descended upon the world, and, as 1930 wore on, the bright prospects described by Thayer Lindsley in his address to the 1929 annual meeting were dimmed considerably. Available cash then indicated by him as in excess of two million dollars had shrunk under the demands of the heavy construction programme carried out during the year. To mention but two items, the refinery addition and repairs had required over a million dollars and the smelter another six hundred thousand.

But, as a result of the market decline, brokers who had undertaken to sell the company's stock, and whose firm commitments had been included in the previous year's estimate of cash resources, were unable to fulfil their undertakings. Consequently it had been necessary to write off $278,000 which in ordinary circumstances would have been available.

Getting a smelter crew was almost as hard as recruiting the original mine crew, but Craig was able to persuade Charles Taylor to leave the former Mond plant at Coniston and throw in his lot with Falconbridge. He with two other experienced smeltermen who could be coaxed from other employment provided the three shift-bosses under whom the Falconbridge smelter crew was organized.

The smelter, blown in on February 4, 1930, treated 71,626 tons of ore in its first year, producing matte in excess of the refinery's capacity to handle it. Despite the inexperience of those who had built it, the smelter had given a minimum of trouble, exceeding its rated capacity and when, at the end of 1930, it was shut down for two months, the cause was not due to any deficiency in itself, or those who, headed by J. R. Gill, were in charge of it.

The blast-furnace was of the usual water-cooled type, ten feet in length by fifty inches at the tuyere level, with four water-jackets fourteen feet by thirty inches on each side. The two convertors were twenty feet by thirteen feet lined with magnesite brick. A matte consisting of eighty-three per cent nickel plus copper was produced.

The cause of the shut-down was financial. While the company still had a substantial balance at the bank, the depressed condition of the metal market resulting in drastically reduced sales, had greatly disturbed Hardy. He, not without difficulty, succeeded in making arrangements for a bank loan against refined nickel in stock, and, as an added precaution, he advised a two-months' shut-down so that expenses might be reduced.

To take advantage of the shut-down and in order to provide work for the married men living on the property, Craig arranged to build a five-foot extension to the blast furnace which later enabled production to be stepped up without the necessity of closing down again. At the same time, additions were made to the housing on the townsite, and it was at this time that the first section of the superintendent's residence was built.

In addition to the depressed condition of the metal market, difficulty was experienced by the company in selling its product because, although it was then the equal of any on the market, the Kristiansand refinery had not previously enjoyed a good reputation. Time was required to assure the trade that nickel bearing the Falconbridge trade-mark was of the highest quality. When, however, this was finally accomplished, the company rapidly gained and held new customers.

Despite these unfavourable factors, the company's agents were able, during 1931, to dispose of 3,205,235 pounds of nickel, which included an order from U.S. Steel, most welcome at that time. The year's sales, although but 52.6 per cent of what was produced, plus that on hand from the previous year, indicated that under normal conditions the plant would be inadequate. It was therefore decided in September, 1932, to build a 250-ton concentrator, a sintering plant and further extend the smelter and crushing equipment. The concentrator and sintering plant made it possible to handle ores which could not be treated by direct-smelting. Following these additions, the daily tonnage rate was increased from 544 tons treated during the first three months of 1933 to 779 tons thereafter.

With the building of the concentrator, Falconbridge gained the addition to its personnel of a man who was eventually to hold an increasingly important position. He was R. C. Mott who, after graduation from Queen's, had joined the staff of Ventures Limited at Sherritt-Gordon and had now come to Falconbridge to take charge of the concentrator.

Falconbridge had weathered the worst of the depression, had increased its plants' capacity, paying for the new equipment out of earnings, and at the end of 1933 was able to show a net profit for the year of $1,122,999.28. Furthermore, during this, its fifth year, the company had paid its first dividend, amounting to twenty-five cents a share on outstanding shares. If proof were needed that this company was on the highroad of success, that was it.

Financial success constitutes the usual criterion and, of course, in an enterprise conducted for gain it is essential, but there are other criteria. One of these consists of the human element, and Falconbridge was also successful in this regard. Perhaps it was one of the results of the obstacles which they had faced together that had developed an unusual *esprit de corps*. Everyone on the payroll seemed imbued with a desire to confound the sceptics by helping to make the concern a success.

During 1934, the inconvenience of handling production from so small a shaft became such that a larger one was decided upon. This was a five-compartment shaft, known as No. 5, which was sunk some 2,400 feet east of No. 1 shaft. Here the depth of the overburden was determined by means of an electrical survey, checked by a bore hole, and established at one hundred feet. In order to counteract the tendency of sand and gravel to cave and also to get through the quicksand, the shaft was sunk inside a steel-plate shield, followed by closely spaced timber sets tightly lagged. When bedrock was reached, a concrete lining was poured inside the timber and continued to the surface, permanent steel sets then being placed in position at six-foot intervals. At the end of the year the shaft had reached a depth of 546 feet.

In conformity with Thayer Lindsley's ideas, the company had continued to safeguard its position and also to increase its possibilities of future expansion by acquiring, by staking or otherwise, property in various parts of the rim. Much of this had been done in the name of the Sudbury Nickel and Copper Company Limited, and in 1934 the holdings of this company were transferred to Falconbridge in return for 40,052 shares of the company's capital stock.

Some of the claims thus secured would in later years prove of great value to Falconbridge and may even provide the determining point between whether the company will be an ordinarily successful one or an extremely important one. And what was once considered but a visionary's dream may some day be transformed into striking reality.

Attention, during 1935, was centred upon the No. 5 shaft, which by year-end had reached a depth of slightly over 1,400 feet, with the principal development level established at 1,200 feet. The year marked a change from the shrinkage method of mining in effect hitherto to the cut-and-fill system, making possible the handling of cleaner ore. In connection with this, fill-pass systems were established at three points to enable sand for back-filling to be introduced into the workings. By the end of the year about twenty-five per cent of ore mined was from cut-and-fill stopes, and this percentage would be increased in later years.

Falconbridge had hit its stride, and during 1936 every department of the mine showed an increase. In that year, 327,783 tons of ore were treated, the refinery producing 11,226,108 pounds of nickel and 4,005,902 pounds of copper, resulting in net sales of $5,178,812.18 and net profits of $1,873,607.05, swelled by security sales amounting to $435,737.77, without which profits from sales would have been $1,437,869.28. Expanding markets for nickel caused the company to undertake further plant extension which, during 1936, required capital expenditures of $2,140,626.14. Nevertheless, the usual dividend of thirty cents a share was paid, leaving a balance in the Earned Surplus Account at the end of the year of $2,799,871.87.

Despite the large increase in acreage acquired the preceding year from the Sudbury Nickel and Copper Company Limited, Ernest Craig's crews were again busy staking, adding during the year over six hundred claims to the company's holdings which with purchases brought the additions to 633 claims.

This year Thayer Lindsley stepped down from the presidency, becoming one of the two vice-presidents, while

Gordon Hardy was installed in his place.   If there is one person more than any other to whom credit for the company's success is due, that person is Gordon Hardy.

Although its ore did not equal in richness that of a Creighton, a Frood or a Levack, Falconbridge had, in its short corporate life, spent on plant and equipment more than six million dollars, paid dividends amounting to $3,713,687.26 and had established a community of upwards of one thousand people.

The year 1937 was one of relative depression throughout Canada, which, however, did not affect Falconbridge's scale of operations.   The plant handled 438,629 tons, the most ever hoisted, and sales were at a record height of $5,862,457.91, but net profits of $1,471,495.07 did not show a corresponding increase.   Higher costs, both of labour and supplies, and lower metal prices, were responsible for this, to which was added a protracted strike at the refinery in Norway.   Ore reserves were increased by over a million tons, bringing the total to 6,332,601, and the ore picture looked promising at a new "bottom level" of 1,750 feet.   As had now become the rule, a dividend of thirty cents a share was paid during the year, bringing the total dividends paid to date to $4,714,962.00.

Through 1938 and 1939, while the world was arming and after the outbreak of war, nickel once more became of prime importance.   Falconbridge continued to expand all along the line until the Germans took over its refinery at Kristiansand on April 9, 1940.   This was a hard blow, causing the company to curtail production until arrangements could be made with Inco to refine its product, but it had nevertheless already established itself as an important factor in Canadian mining.   The scoffers had long since been silenced.   Its great period was yet to come, but already it could be said that here at last was a company competent to stand with Inco and Mond as the only ones in the Canadian nickel industry's history of more than half a century that could successfully meet the challenge of nickel.

# XVIII

# *Mines Respond to War's Urgency*

T HE REARMAMENT PROGRAMME BROUGHT
about by Hitler's belligerency increased
the demand for metal, especially nickel. In 1936 the
Canadian industry produced 169,739,393 pounds of nickel,
which jumped to 224,905,046 pounds in 1937 and to
245,557,871 pounds in 1940. Falconbridge and Inco were
both geared to their greatest production ever, but the loss
of the former's refinery after Hitler went into Norway
(April 9, 1940) hampered that company until arrangements
could be made with Inco for the refining of its product.
Falconbridge's great period of expansion was yet to come,
but from 1941 to the end of the war its production steadily
increased.

In 1945, Falconbridge's production was only slightly
greater than the low of 1940, but beginning in 1946 a steady
gain was made which, in 1950, was augmented by ore shipments from the company's new McKim mine, adjacent to
Inco's Murray mine, bringing total production to 928,835
tons. In 1951, McKim supplied 155,961 tons which, added
to the 930,164 tons produced by the Falconbridge mine,
put the company's production for the first time over the
million-ton mark, with 1,086,125 tons. In 1952, while the

Falconbridge mine fell slightly below the previous year, McKim's 224,774 tons brought total production to 1,212,856 tons.

Increasing demand for nickel has brought three new nickel-copper mines into production in the Sudbury district since 1952. The first of these, owned by East Rim Nickel Mines Limited, is located in MacLennan township where the company holds nine claims. The second, owned by Milnet Mines Limited, is also located on the east rim, in Parkin township. The third, owned by Nickel Offsets Limited, as its name implies, an offset deposit, is located beyond the north rim, in Foy and Bowell townships, comprising approximately 1,912 acres. During 1953, all three were shipping ore by truck to the Falconbridge smelter.

Inco's expansion during the war and after was truly remarkable. In the war years the company produced and delivered to the Allies for military and other essential purposes about 1,500,000,000 pounds of nickel in all forms and 1,750,000,000 pounds of refined copper and large quantities of the very necessary platinum metals. Inco has stated that the tonnage of ore mined during the war was equal to that produced by it and its predecessors in the preceding fifty-four years of their existence.

In order to provide this greatly increased production, the company invested approximately $150,000,000 in opening additional mining properties, sinking shafts and installing surface and underground plant and equipment, as well as the enlargement of concentrating, smelting and refining works. Not only were these plant-extensions carried out without hampering production, but production was greatly increased at the same time.

Open-pit mining, the earliest method adopted after discovery of the mines in the eighties, was still in use, in addition to underground mining, at the Creighton and the Frood (later, at the Stobie as well). By nature, it was admirably adapted to expansion, and production from the pits was stepped up sharply, eventually providing over forty per cent of the company's ore.

This type of mining, however, has definite limits, and in anticipation of those limits being reached, a ten-year programme of underground expansion was launched with a view to mining, hoisting and treating 13,000,000 tons of ore a year.   This programme was begun under the direction of Donald MacAskill, then vice-president of Canadian operations.   He did not live to see it completed, that task being transferred to his successor, R. Leslie Beattie, who also died, but not before the end of the programme was in sight.

The Murray mine, with whose chequered career the reader is already familiar, was brought into production, as well as the Stobie section of the Frood-Stobie mine. But, as in the past, the company's chief endeavours centred about the fabulous Creighton.   Here it was planned to recover, by newly-developed mining methods, immense deposits of lower grade ore, concentrate it at the mine and convey the concentrates by pipe-line the seven and one-half miles to the Copper Cliff smelter.

In the earlier years shrinkage mining, as already described, was the rule in most of the underground mining, but with greater depth a general change was made to cut-and-fill and square-set methods which became standard in working the higher grade ores.  With improvement in metallurgical practice and the development of low-cost bulk-mining methods, economic recovery of lower grade ores became possible by means of caving and blasthole mining.

These methods can be used only where wide deposits exist, such as at Creighton and Frood-Stobie. The caving method consists of undercutting large slabs of ore which eventually break loose of their own weight and in their fall disintegrate, making unnecessary the use as well as the cost of explosives.  Blasthole mining follows the same general principle, except that caving is induced by blasting.

In addition to the Creighton and Frood-Stobie, blast-hole mining is being used at Levack and also at the Murray, and by the time the underground programme is completed will probably account for the greater part of the company's millfeed.

Operations at the Creighton will be described because they afford the best illustration of Inco's mining and reduction methods. Two principal types of mineralization make up the Creighton deposit. The higher grade ore consists of a breccia containing massive sulphides in irregular patches, stringers or lenses, usually found close to the contact of the norite with the older rocks. The lower grade ore consists of norite with ore minerals finely disseminated throughout. Breccia ore at the Creighton has been mined out from the surface to the 30 level, and it is the disseminated ore remaining in the 1,750 feet from the 28 level to the surface that is now being recovered by caving.

In order to handle ore from the caving operation, No. 7 shaft, designed for ore hoisting only, was sunk initially to a depth of 2,056 feet. Concrete-lined, it has two skip compartments separated by a manway and pipe compartment. The skips carry fifteen tons. The headframe is a concrete structure 197 feet high and with the hoisthouse is an integral part of the concentrator building. Ore from the receiving bin in the headframe is fed directly to the concentrator crushing plant.

The hoist, with a capacity of 650 tons an hour, is automatic, operated by push-button from the loading pocket. Run by electricity and free from clanging signal bells, the hoist at Creighton No. 7 shaft is a model of quiet efficiency.

All ore is crushed underground, flowing by gravity to the crusher station at the 28 level. Here two sixty-six by forty-eight-inch crushers have each a capacity of 590 tons of ore an hour, crushing it to a maximum of six inches. From each crusher the ore falls to a 1,500-ton concrete-lined bin on the 30 level, from which it is carried by a forty-eight-inch conveyor 1,850 feet to the loading station storage bin at No. 7 shaft.

The handling of ore underground has also been revolutionized. The lowly mucker whose duty it once was to shovel broken ore into trams pushed by hand is no longer seen. In his place are scrapers or "slushers" which propel the ore along slusher drifts from which it drops through chutes directly into cars hauled by electric locomotives that are dumped by automatic tipples into underground ore bins.

Owing to the growing unrest in world affairs and the increased demand for nickel, the Creighton mill, designed in 1948 to treat 6,000 tons a day, was first stepped up to 10,000, and later to 12,000 tons. This includes 2,000 tons from Creighton No. 5 shaft, two-thirds of a mile distant. This ore, from which the magnetic portion is removed for direct smelting before being transferred by conveyor to the mill, is of higher grade and is kept separate throughout the milling process.

McArthur and Peters, could they return for a moment to the scene of their former activities, would marvel at the modern, fireproof concentrator building of steel, concrete and tile, seventy feet high, covering an area 440 by 175 feet. Built on level ground, it is laid out in three parallel sections: the bin section, containing in addition to the twenty-thousand-ton ore bin, the offices, change house and storage bays for grinding steel; the crushing and grinding aisle and repair bay; and the flotation aisle also containing reagent storage rooms and classifiers of the sand fill plant.

The grinding section is divided into four units, each containing a rod mill, a ball mill and a classifier. Ore is fed direct to the rod mill, and the rod mill discharge is pumped to the classifier. The latter feeds the ball mill with which it operates in closed circuit.

The flotation process consists of a straight recovery circuit from which a bulk copper-nickel concentrate is produced. Flotation feed is pumped to a six-way distributor and flows by gravity to six parallel rows of cells comprising a total of 144, twenty-four to a row, arranged in three banks of eight in series. One 25 h.p. motor operates two cells. Various flotation reagents (such as pine oil, lime, sodium silicate, etc.) are added to the circuit at intervals. Rubber-covered disc impellers keep the pulp in motion.

Not the least important part of the saving effected by the Creighton operation is the elimination of a large part of the former cost of transporting concentrates to Copper Cliff. Already tailings from the Copper Cliff concentrator were being pumped through wood-stave pipe mounted on a wooden trestle to 1,100-acre disposal grounds located more than half-way to Creighton. It was therefore decided to use the same tailing disposal ground for Creighton, building three and a half miles of trestle and wood-stave pipe to meet those from Copper Cliff. The pipe line reaches a maximum elevation forty-eight feet higher than the Creighton mill and drops ninety-eight feet in the final two miles to Copper Cliff. Five pumping stations are required to keep the contents in motion. Little difficulty has been experienced due to the extremely cold weather in winter, temperature loss during the coldest weather being not more than 2° F. per mile.

Completion of Inco's expansion programme has made it possible for the company to undertake delivery to the Defence Materials Procurement Agency of the United States government of 120,000,000 pounds of nickel and 100,000,000 pounds of copper, deliveries to begin in December, 1953, at the rate of 2,000,000 pounds of nickel and 1,666,666 pounds of copper a month, continuing until 1958.

Another factor making possible this undertaking was the successful outcome of experiments conducted over a period of years by the company's research departments for the economic recovery of iron ore from Sudbury nickel-copper ores, as announced, September 17, 1953, by J. R. Gordon, vice-president and general manager of Inco's Canadian operations. This was news important to all the world for it meant that henceforth 1,000,000 tons of high-grade iron ore, hitherto going off in slag, would become available to industry.

Mr. Gordon announced that construction would begin immediately of a $16,000,000 plant in the Copper Cliff area. The plant will produce iron ore containing at least sixty-five per cent natural iron and less than two per cent silica, much higher in grade than any now produced in North America. At the start it will treat 1,000 tons a day of nickel-bearing pyrrhotite removed from ore in the early stages of processing at Copper Cliff.

This new process makes possible the treatment of ores hitherto considered uneconomical. This is perhaps the most far-reaching (at the moment) of a number of important metallurgical findings of Inco's research engineers, such, for example, as copper-nickel separation by controlled cooling and flotation of matte and oxygen-flash smelting of copper concentrates.

The latter, conducted previously on an experimental basis, was carried out commercially in 1952.

Initiation of this process made possible large-scale production of sulphur dioxide by Canadian Industries Limited in a new plant built for the purpose at Copper Cliff. Since sulphur is an essential in the manufacture of sulphite pulp an available supply close at hand should be of advantage to the pulp and paper industry of Ontario and Quebec.

An attempt has been made in these pages to give an account of the long and complicated history of the International Nickel Company of Canada, Limited, and its predecessors as an integral part of the story of Sudbury Basin. By and large, it is a remarkable success story. The record of those who failed, partially given here, supplies mute evidence in support of this statement. In the almost three-quarters of a century only two other companies—Mond and Falconbridge—have succeeded.

Survival although vital does not, however, constitute the whole picture. How a person or a company is regarded by his or its associates is also important. At times, Inco has gone its way without much regard for others and in consequence has sometimes been unpopular. While it still goes its own way, the attitude of the community toward it is far from unfriendly. The people of Sudbury Basin have come to accept the big company for what it is and to take pride in its achievement, for it is impossible to come in contact with its operations and not experience a feeling of admiration for its obvious efficiency.

And this efficiency is not confined merely to the operation of plants and equipment or the control of complicated scientific processes. It applies as well in the field of human relations.

In 1928, Inco established its retirement system providing both service and total disability pensions for life, and benefit payments at death, the cost of which is assumed by the company without requiring any contributions from employees. Under this plan, for example, an employee who retires at age sixty-five after thirty years' service, and whose annual remuneration during his final five years averaged $3,000, receives a life pension of $1,530 a year. During the first quarter-century of the system, 1,955 employees had been retired on service or disability pensions and 2,179 beneficiaries of former employees had received death benefit payments.

Until World War II Inco's employees were not unionized. Previous efforts by union organizers received little encouragement from the company. But, in 1944, when the federal government, under authority of the War Measures Act passed Order-in-Council P.C. 1003, establishing the Dominion Labour Relations Regulations, applicable to all essential war industries, and providing for collective bargaining, the company proceeded to enter into agreements with the certified representatives of its employees.

When the Regulations ceased to have legal force, the company continued to recognize the union designated by a majority of its employees concerned and amicable labour relations have since prevailed.

Important as the human element may be, it is sometimes in danger of being dwarfed by the giant machines which men have made. Inco's great smelter at Copper Cliff, with its roaring furnaces and three great stacks, two over five hundred feet high, perpetually belching smoke, dominates the scene. But the batteries of grinding machines and equipment for separating and refining metals, endlessly performing their functions with scientific precision, while less awe-inspiring than the great smelter, help to fill the beholder with greater respect for the ingenuity of man.

# XIX

# *From Gossan to Geology*

FOR HALF A CENTURY THE MINES STAKED by the early prospectors supplied most of the needs of the mining companies. The Canadian Copper Company, first in the field, facing little competition, was able to secure ore reserves sufficient to safeguard its production and that of its successor well into the future. The Mond Nickel Company, coming later, and always fearful that it might run short of millfeed, went into the market and bought several of what proved to be the most productive properties in Sudbury Basin. In fact, by chance or otherwise, the orebodies acquired by Mond have been the mainstay of production in the district for many years. British America Nickel Corporation, coming in still later, was also able to meet its requirements without resorting to unproven prospects. Its failure and the purchase of its assets on behalf of Inco increased the latter's already ample holdings which, as a result of its amalgamation with Mond, gave it control of the most promising properties in Sudbury Basin.

To this there was one notable exception. In 1916-1917, the Longyear Company of Minneapolis had drilled the former Edison property in Falconbridge township and a number of adjacent claims staked by W. E. Smith on their behalf, disclosing a continuous orebody extending along the strike for a distance of 7,500 feet. This, in 1928, had been acquired by Falconbridge Nickel Mines Limited and in the interval had been energetically developed.

FALCONBRIDGE No. 5 SHAFT HEADFRAME AND MINE BUILDINGS
FALCONBRIDGE No. 1 SHAFT HEADFRAME AND MINE BUILDINGS

THAYER LINDSLEY

JOSEPH ERRINGTON
J. GORDON HARDY
H. J. FRASER

Thayer Lindsley, first president of Falconbridge, had shortly relinquished that post to J. Gordon Hardy who, with Ernest Craig as mine manager, chiefly conducted the company's affairs. Lindsley, having assumed the position of vice-president, was not greatly concerned with the details of mine management, but he had not ceased to be intrigued with the geology of Sudbury Basin. Not convinced that existing mines had exhausted its possibilities, he hired Terence Connolly, formerly on the Bradleys' geological staff, to set up a geological department at Falconbridge. Connolly was asked to make a comprehensive report on the district with a view to acquiring mining property that might contain hitherto unsuspected orebodies, and this programme was continued for several years with the assistance of Stanley Davidson, as consultant, under Connolly's successors, F. M. Galbraith, R. C. Hart and D. R. Lockhead.

In the years previous to World War II, Falconbridge began acquiring properties, either by staking or purchase, on or near the contact along the 110-mile periphery of the Basin. These were explored by magnetometer and when anomalies were found were tested by drilling. One such anomaly, on the north rim, west of Inco's Levack mine, where no outcrop existed, was drilled in the fall of 1935, disclosing an extensive orebody. This has since been developed and is known as the Hardy mine, named after the former Falconbridge president.

Exploration was largely discontinued during the war, but when the war was over the programme was continued. In the meantime, H. J. Fraser, formerly with Inco's department of geology and subsequently a professor at the California Institute of Technology, had become mine manager at Falconbridge and in 1947 was to become vice-president and general manager. During the war, on leave of absence from Caltech, Fraser had served with the Office of Economic Warfare in Washington after the United States entered the war, having charge of matters pertaining to the purchase abroad of nickel, manganese, chromium and iron. It was in this connection that he had come under the eye of Thayer Lindsley, who urged him to come to Falconbridge.

During 1945, a substantial lens of ore had been located by diamond drilling on ground adjacent to and east of the Murray mine. Previously, holes put down in the vicinity of small outcroppings along the contact had failed to find an orebody but, in accordance with their theory concerning the structure, the geologists recommended that the drills be moved a certain distance off the contact to the north, and there the ore was found. Further drilling the following year proved the existence of sufficient ore of good grade to justify the sinking of a shaft. This was begun in the summer of 1947 and by the end of the year had reached a depth of 477 feet. All major buildings and installations were completed in 1948, the shaft bottomed at 1,421 feet, with drifting begun on four levels. By the end of the next year, drifting on these levels had confirmed tonnages and ore grades indicated by drilling, and development ore amounting to 15,896 tons had been shipped to the smelter at Falconbridge, thus establishing the McKim mine as the first new nickel producer in Sudbury Basin since the Falconbridge mine itself had begun operations in 1930. In 1951 and subsequent years it continued to ship ore beyond its rated 500 tons a day.

Falconbridge was sinking two new shafts in 1951, one at what is called the East mine, 4,500 feet east of the main shaft (No. 5), and the other at Hardy mine. At the end of the year the former had reached a depth of 245 feet and the latter 1,028 feet.

In the meantime, the exploration programme had been proceeding steadily. In 1937, Falconbridge bought the Mount Nickel property in Blezard township, staked in 1885 by James Stobie. The Great Lakes Copper Company had opened it up in 1889 but had failed, not because of lack of ore but because the refining process upon which the company depended would not work. Although a shaft was completed on the property in 1953, the orebody is relatively limited, but this was not the main objective of Falconbridge geologists. The Blezard mine, staked in 1885 and operated from 1889 to 1893 by the Dominion Mineral Company, was what the company had its eye on in the belief that a small outcrop on the property would be found to expand into a considerable orebody inside the Mount Nickel boundary. This was confirmed in 1941 and may easily become a major proposition whenever Falconbridge is ready to open it up.

Despite the possibility of finding ore in spots along the south rim, as at McKim, Mount Nickel and Blezard, Fraser believed that greater results might be secured by concentrating upon the north rim. Already the Hardy mine had been developed out of a magnetometer prospect. Another orebody (known as the "Boundary") was indicated by pre-war drilling a short distance east of the Hardy mine. By the end of 1953 its extent had not been fully determined, but enough was known to justify the belief that it will prove to be a substantial orebody.

Important as these various new properties are likely to be in determining the fortunes of the Falconbridge company, the fruits of successful geological deduction were to be more fully exemplified. To the east of Inco's Levack mine, a small weed-filled lake called Fecunis (fe, cu, ni, s), lies at a point on the norite contact where a well-marked fault has thrown the rim out of alignment. No ore could be seen at the surface but Falconbridge geologists, now headed by D. R. Lockhead, deduced that deep beneath the surface a large orebody probably existed. It would be an expensive matter to find out but, with Lindsley's and Fraser's concurrence, a drilling programme was decided upon.

During the winter of 1948-1949, drills were set up on the ice prepared to go to 3,000 feet or deeper if necessary. In March, the drill cut a small ore zone at about 1,200 feet, as was expected. According to the theory, this was the regular norite contact, but it was believed that a larger orebody would be encountered much deeper. The drills continued and when the break-up occurred they were transferred to barges specially designed for the purpose. The geologists probably held their breath as the drills neared the depth at which ore might be encountered. The result was a triumph for pure geological reasoning: there was the ore where it should be and in sufficient amounts to assume a mining operation for many years to come.

In 1944, Falconbridge had bought the Strathcona property, staked in the early days by an Indian on behalf of T. B. Ross and Donald MacTavish, officers of the Hudson's Bay Company. On this property there is a relatively small deposit of ore which shows on the surface and which the company proposes to work by open pit. But, as usual, the geologists had their eye on larger quarry. Drilling along the contact westward from the outcrop a large deposit of medium grade ore was encountered at depth in 1951. The name Strathcona has been retained for this deposit and the open pit workings will be known as the Longvack mine.

As a result of drilling, chiefly in this portion of the north rim, the company's indicated ore reserves were increased from 15,147,500 tons at the end of 1950 to 32,987,000 at the end of 1952, for most of which the Fecunis Lake prospect was responsible.

These extensive prospecting operations did not interfere with the development of other properties. At McKim during 1952, provision was made for crushing ore under-ground by the excavation of a station below the 1,175 level and for the installation of the necessary equipment. At the Hardy mine, the shaft was bottomed in May at 1,427 feet, with all stations cut. A permanent steel headframe was erected in place of the temporary one used during sinking operations, and development was commenced on all levels. At the end of the year excavation was under way for a crusher station at the 1,060 level. The surface plant and a number of buildings in the townsite were completed as well as a two-mile railway spur connecting with the Canadian Pacific Railway.

To treat the increasing quantities of ore being shipped to the plant at Falconbridge, a fourth converter was installed in July, 1953, and a third blast furnace and settler were put into operation toward the end of October. The first regular shipment of ore was made from the Hardy mine to Falconbridge on October 22, 1953.

Preparations were completed for the building of a concentrating plant at the Hardy mine, consisting of magnetic separation, followed by flotation, to be ready by the fall of 1954, and a similar plant is proposed for Fecunis to be ready probably in 1957. Such operations must be planned a long time ahead and also take a long time to complete.

The major activity of the Falconbridge staff for several years to come will be concerned with Fecunis where, to start with, two shafts are being sunk, the combined depth of which is 7,285 feet. This shaft-sinking constitutes the largest job of its kind ever contracted for at one time in Canada. No. 1 shaft, fourteen by twenty feet, will be sunk 3,945 feet, but the mine will be operated from an adit which extends 650 feet into the hill, ending in a runaround, with the shaft in the centre, 198 feet below the top of the hill. Ore will be hoisted to the adit level, transported by conveyor to an underground storage bin and from there by a second conveyor to the mill, located at the foot of the hill.

No. 1 shaft is expected to be completed by the end of 1955 and will be the hoisting shaft, while No. 2, approximately eight by twenty-four feet, on lower ground nearer the lake, will be the one from which drives will be run into the ore in order to get it out. The two shafts will be connected underground at convenient intervals.

With increasing production from mines on the north rim, it will probably be necessary for Falconbridge to provide additional smelting facilities, and it will also be necessary eventually to provide refining facilities on this side of the Atlantic to take care of markets in North

America, likely in future to absorb a large share of the company's production. There is also the question of the utilization of the iron and sulphur content of the ore.

Nevertheless, beginning in 1949, an extensive programme of modernization has been carried out at Kristiansand. The plant has been increased to the point where it can cope with the company's minimum requirements of 35,000,000 pounds of nickel a year. In addition, facilities have been provided for the separate recovery of cobalt. S. B. Steen continues as resident manager of the refinery, while Anton Gronningsater, the company's oldest employee in years of service, is consulting metallurgist.

Perhaps one of the best illustrations of the change that has taken place in the nickel industry is that exemplified by the attitude of governments. Ritchie had to plead to have the metal tested. Later, during the twenties, the nickel mines closed down for a period through lack of markets. But as a result of many essential uses developed by research during the intervening years, nickel was one of the first metals to go under government allocation during World War II. Again, when the Korean crisis developed nickel was promptly placed under allocation. As a result of its greatly increased importance, governments began to have a keen interest in accumulating a stockpile of nickel for use in such emergencies.

To this end, the Defence Materials Procurement Agency of the United States government has contracted with Falconbridge for the purchase of very substantial amounts of nickel over the next ten years. These contracts necessitate a very considerable increase in Falconbridge's production facilities and the government has furnished financial assistance for this programme of increased production.

Naturally the number of employees has been greatly expanded to take care of this accelerated activity. At the end of 1952, the number employed in Canada was 2,412 and 1,088 in Norway, making a total of 3,500 of whom 3,140 were engaged in nickel-copper production. Since April 1, 1951, a contributory pension plan has been in effect to which both company and employees contribute on the basis of five per cent of the employees' earnings. The plan provides for the transfer, in certain circumstances, of all or part of the company's contribution in cases of termination of employment. Provision is made for pensions in the event of total disability. Normal retirement age is sixty-five but an employee may retire at an earlier age on reduced pension. A somewhat similar plan had been in effect for staff members since 1942.

When J. Gordon Hardy retired from the presidency in 1945 his place was taken by L. K. Brindley, who remained in that position until April, 1947, when Thayer Lindsley again resumed the office with H. J. Fraser as assistant to the president and general manager. The following year Fraser became vice-president and general manager, his former position being assumed by R. C. Mott, formerly smelter superintendent, who had been with the company since 1933.

The increasing activity culminating in 1953 made necessary certain staff changes. R. C. Mott, as manager of the Mining and Reduction Division, became responsible for all operations in the Sudbury area, with R. M. Oliver, general superintendent, and Ed. Healy, assistant, in charge of operations at mines in the south range—Falconbridge, East, McKim and Mount Nickel; and Harold North, and D. R. Lockhead, assistant, in charge of the mines being developed on the north range—Hardy, Boundary, Fecunis, Strathcona and Longvack.

Beginning in 1928 with an undeveloped orebody, lacking both road and railway connection with the nearest settlement, Falconbridge, after the lapse of a quarter of a century, now operates five mines, with six others awaiting development. Once more the Sudbury nickel industry is in the hands of two principal companies. For many years their relative size and importance was such that it remained virtually a one-company affair. That Falconbridge, following scientific procedures, has been able to assume a position of increasing importance in the nickel industry is cause for satisfaction on the part of all concerned.

# XX

# *Nickel Metropolis*

NOT MANY CITIES ARE BUILT SIMPLY because they are pleasant places in which to live. In some cases this undoubtedly contributes toward a city's growth, but in general much more is needed. To grow and prosper, a city must have a functional basis. This, cities in the Shield must certainly have. But for the presence of nickel-copper ore, Sudbury as such would not have existed. In the years to come, other cities will arise in different parts of the Shield not because their sites are suitable but because they have grown up about a mine, a pulp and paper plant or some other indigenous industry.

Many drift-covered localities in the Shield might provide a site for a city, but it is more than likely that they will be built where rocks predominate. This will mean that in most cases basements and foundations, streets and excavations for water mains and sewers, must be blasted out of the solid rock.

Water pipes will need to be protected against low temperatures in winter. It is a notorious fact that serious fires are much more common in extremely cold weather than at any other time, and firefighters must not find their hydrants frozen when they need water.

For nearly three-quarters of a century Sudbury has grappled with such problems and has learned to solve them. Rex Martindale, for fifty years in charge of Sudbury's waterworks, knows all there is to know about such problems.

# SUDBURY CITY URBAN LAND USE

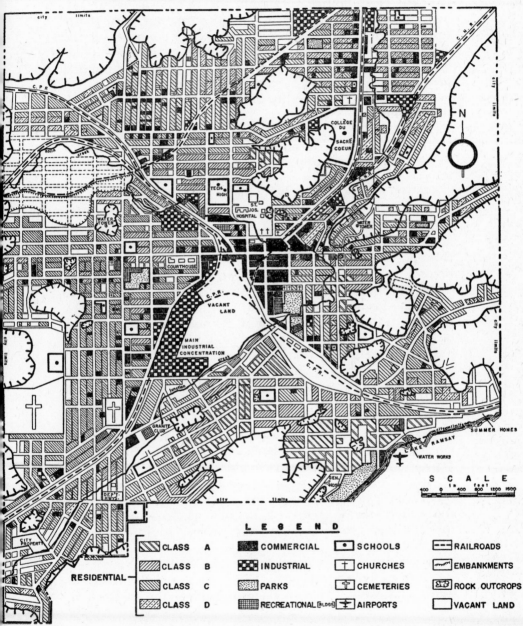

**LEGEND**

RESIDENTIAL —
CLASS A
CLASS B
CLASS C
CLASS D

COMMERCIAL
INDUSTRIAL
PARKS
RECREATIONAL [BLDGS]

SCHOOLS
CHURCHES
CEMETERIES
AIRPORTS

RAILROADS
EMBANKMENTS
ROCK OUTCROPS
VACANT LAND

R. P. BAINE

In many cases houses were built, some of brick, before any waterworks existed, or were extended to that part of the town. In order to install water and sewer connections, the waterworks department has had to tunnel its way under houses built solidly upon the rock. Yet it is Martindale's proud boast that never has the city been called upon to pay even a dollar's damages for breakages in connection with the installation of such services. Furthermore, the cost to the city of pipes burst by frost is as low as anywhere else. Sudbury, therefore, in addition to being the forerunner of Shield cities to come, provides blueprints for their guidance.

In the beginning was the railway. If it is responsible for Sudbury's existence, it is also responsible for many of its problems, past, present and future. The town grew up along the railway, which means that the railway now cuts through its busiest section, interrupting east-west traffic at several intersections. The Sault Ste. Marie line, branching off to the west, divides Sudbury into quarters on that side, while the former Stobie branch, on the other, now used to transfer traffic between the C.P.R. and the C.N.R., cuts across the busiest corner in the city, taking a slice off many important business sites, including the postoffice.

Rocky ridges give the city a crow's-foot pattern, extending in finger-like strips, without symmetry or system. The entrance from the southeast is through gaunt, bare hills where fire and sulphur have destroyed nearly every vestige of vegetation, leaving the countryside as devoid of living matter as the dark side of the moon, an aspect which only a Dante in his worst moments might envisage.

Inside the city, however, trees and lawns to a certain extent mask the black rocks and, tucked between outcrops, occasional sylvan spots are found. Houses perched on rocky ledges break the bare monotony, adding welcome patches of colour. Here is a case where raw nature is improved by even the poorest of man's handiwork.

Bare rocky territory generally borders the Basin on the south and west. In the eastern section, the bedrock is buried under heavy overburden, submerging what otherwise would be a series of rocky hills and ridges similar to those elsewhere.

Inside the Basin, the flat plain is relieved by a few low hills and cut by the tributaries of Vermilion river, itself winding in a series of ox-bows along the valley from northeast to southwest. Fields, farm houses and dairy cattle seem out of place so soon have the rocky hills been left behind.

The north rim presents the pleasantest aspect of all. Here, although hills are rugged, the bush is still thick, the rocks more generally covered by soil. Attractive townsites for the mines being developed there should be possible with much less effort than in most other places around the Basin's rim.

Chief of the mining towns, Copper Cliff, with a population of 4,000, is much more pleasant than formerly. Since it is Inco's headquarters, a larger percentage of substantial dwellings have been built there than in other mining towns. While its surroundings are still as gaunt as ever, the high smelter stacks and the greater amount of sulphur diverted from the fumes have made grass and trees possible again. Inco has spent some money in developing a park near the centre of the town, adding greatly to its appearance.

Coniston, eight miles southeast of Sudbury, with about 2,500 people clustered around its smelter, occupies a strategic position beside the C.P.R. mainline and between the C.N.R. and C.P.R. Toronto branches, but it has little else to commend it. Situated in the dreariest section of the most forbidding region in the Sudbury area, it reflects the worst aspects of communities inhabited by people whose only reason for living where they do is that they also work there.

Levack, with about 2,000 people, serves the mine of that name on the north rim. In contrast to Coniston its surroundings are much more pleasant because of the more pleasing nature of the terrain, and this helps the looks of residences even though they may be similar in type to those in less favoured towns. Furthermore, on account of increased production at the mine, the town contains many new buildings.

This also applies to Creighton which, as we know, has expanded greatly in recent years. The older residential sections follow no set plan and exhibit all the defects of such towns, the houses varying greatly in appearance and apparent comfort. To take care of new workers at the mine, however, Inco has built a residential community with adequate commercial facilities about two miles south of the mine. Called Lively, after a former company officer, it represents a new departure in supplying the residential needs of a large mine, and in this respect occupies the opposite pole from Coniston. It also represents an intelligent approach to one of the important problems of personnel relations.

All the towns mentioned above are associated with Inco mines, but Falconbridge, as its name implies, is the headquarters of Falconbridge Nickel Mines Limited. With a population of some 1,500, it is located on comparatively level ground which, because of the absence of rock, makes for easier planning than is the case with most other company towns in Sudbury district. The company has taken full advantage of this in laying out the townsite and designing the buildings, and in the result has achieved an absence of the usual monotonous uniformity.

Sudbury is the centre upon which all other communities in the district depend for the greater part of their recreation and social life. It is their metropolis. But despite its 50,000 people and its twenty-odd years as a city, it is still very much an overgrown town, quite immature despite its size. In the first place, while in thirty years its population has increased by over 500 per cent, only 153 acres have been added to its area. It is the most congested town in Ontario. With an estimated population in 1950 of 47,054, representing 17.71 persons per acre, a comparison with nine other Ontario cities from Oshawa, with 29,771 people, occupying 3,585 acres, to Kitchener with 43,084 people and

3,470 acres, not one equals Sudbury in density of population. The nearest is Kingston, with 32,924 people in an area of 2,410 acres, or 13.66 to the acre.

In 1950, John Bland and Harold Spence-Sales, of the School of Architecture at McGill University, conducted a survey of the Sudbury area, reporting their findings and recommendations to the mayor and board of aldermen. Their chief recommendation was that the city limits be extended to include all the areas within which urban expansion might be expected during the following five years, and that the appropriate minister of the provincial government be asked to designate the City of Sudbury as the responsible authority for the control of land subdivision within the district.

They recommended that the existing Sudbury District Planning Commission be dissolved and that a Town Planning Commission be appointed whose members should "not be solely representative of financial and real estate interests, but should also be representative of societies and interests concerned with public welfare," and that a Town Planning Officer be appointed as soon as possible.

They recommended that land already in possession of the city be used for recreational purposes and not otherwise disposed of; that certain areas be restricted to commercial purposes; and that steps be taken to examine into the circumstances of vacant and derelict land in the heart of the city in order to bring it into more economical use.

No action has been taken with respect to these recommendations, nor has any practicable alternative been adopted. It is probable that in the end, as in the case of metropolitan Toronto, the legislature will be compelled to set up a competent authority to undertake the necessary action, for it is no more likely in Sudbury than in Toronto that adjoining municipalities with conflicting interests will compose their conflicts, even though the lives and happiness of an increasing number of people depend upon these problems being systematically and economically dealt with.

Sudbury is both a simple and a complex community, sometimes simple to the point of naïvety and at others bafflingly complex.   It is preponderantly a community of young people.   Walk the length of Elm and Durham at any time and the streets will be thronged with people of both sexes mostly on the under side of forty.   Then, it is a polyglot community.   Sometimes it seems that one can walk for blocks on Elm or Durham without hearing a word of English, while at other times everyone will be talking English, some it is true with varying accents, but English, nevertheless.

Few native-born Sudburians have yet risen to prominence in the life of the community.   Of the twenty-three mayors since the town was incorporated in 1893, only two—J. A. Laberge and W. J. Laforest—were born in Sudbury. James M. Cooper, who succeeded Edmond Proulx as District Judge in 1950, is the only native-born Sudburian to hold that office, as he was also the first to win a seat in the legislature (1937).   Welland S. Gemmell, first elected as member for Sudbury in 1948, successively Minister of Mines and Minister of Lands and Forests, was born at Whitefish.

Although J. J. Frawley, an Ottawa lawyer with more than a local reputation, and Leslie Fournier, a professor at Princeton, may be said to have distinguished themselves outside of Sudbury, they are unknown to most Sudburians who invariably nominate a hockey player as most outstanding.

It is almost impossible to find a common denominator for Sudbury, to find a typical Sudburian, but many will agree that Mr. Sudbury when found will strongly resemble William S. Beaton, whose eleven successive terms as mayor seem scarcely possible in a place where political opinions swing back and forth in such fierce emotional tides as in Sudbury.

W. S. Beaton, "Bill" to all who have known him longer than a few minutes, was born in 1896 on a farm in East Gwillimbury, and at an age when most youngsters are still in school began working in Toronto for the C.P.R. Eventually transferred to North Bay as assistant chief clerk, he was moved to Sudbury in 1921, and promptly adopted the place.

Resigning from the C.P.R. in 1927, Beaton went into the insurance business. A genial, cheerful extrovert, genuinely interested in people, fortunate in having a clever wife, he did well, taking time off only to indulge an inordinate love of sport, any sort of sport, from running to boxing. Always on one committee or another, he managed sports and took part in them.

Such a man was fated to get into politics sooner or later, and in 1937 he was elected to the city council at the head of the poll in McCormick ward and re-elected in the two succeeding years. Then he ran for mayor, but his turn had not yet come, and he was defeated by W. J. Laforest. However, the following year he succeeded and for the next ten terms the people of Sudbury chose him as their mayor. Eventually he was beaten by Dan Jessup. Many who had repeatedly voted for him switched in 1951, not because they had anything against Bill Beaton, but because they felt that someone else should have a chance or he would become mayor in perpetuity.

While Beaton is typical of Sudbury in his thinking and reactions, he has done much to mould the city in his own image. Perhaps little help was needed from him, but the city is much more interested in sports than in other aspects of community activity. Not that he neglected measures for the people's welfare, but it comes naturally to him to be interested in providing more playground space, and while Sudbury is still deficient in this respect, the situation might have been worse had it not been for his efforts.

During his regime, both the Sudbury General Hospital, operated by the Sisters of St. Joseph, and the Sudbury and Algoma Sanatorium were begun, but he is perhaps proudest of the Sudbury Community Arena and Civic Centre with which he was associated from the beginning. The arena, with a capacity of 5,400, is on Elgin Street, on the former site of one of Sudbury's oldest schools, almost across the street from the C.P.R. station.

The arena was opened in November, 1951, and cost well over a million dollars, exclusive of the value of the site and the equipment, which was largely donated. In a sense, it symbolizes Sudbury. In proportion to population, it is larger than Toronto's Maple Leaf Gardens. Its location in the centre of a busy commercial district, adding to already badly congested motor traffic, is typical of the headlong manner in which Sudburians sometimes pursue an interest without regard for other considerations.

On June 22, 1948, W. E. Mason died, ending a life that for forty years had been intimately linked with the history of Sudbury. Very little had happened in that time in which Mason had not had a hand. Having no children and his home life not a happy one, he had devoted himself with untiring energy to the double task of building up his paper and developing Sudbury. Both activities proved profitable for him. His faith in the future of Sudbury never wavered and he acquired a great deal of property which in time became very valuable. He was interested, in addition, in many varied enterprises. In 1926, he took over the Grand Theatre, and in 1935, he founded the 1,000-watt radio station, C.K.S.O., increased to 5,000 watts in 1946. (A second station, C.H.N.O., owned by a local company and managed by René Riel, was established in 1947 to broadcast in both French and English).

When Mason died he left his estate to a board of trustees under the chairmanship of George M. Miller, Q.C., to administer at their discretion in the interest of Sudbury. The *Star*, which had become a daily the day war began in 1939, was sold to a group headed by James R. Meakes, formerly general manager under Mason, and has since been published by Sudbury Daily Star Limited, with Miller as president and Meakes as publisher and general manager. C.K.S.O. was acquired by a company headed by Miller and the same directors as the *Star* company, and, in 1953, the

Headframe and Mine Buildings, East Rim Nickel Mines

AERIAL VIEW OF FALCONBRIDGE TOWNSITE, SMELTER, REDUCTION WORKS AND SHAFT HEADFRAMES

first commercial television station in Canada, was established by another company having officers identical with those of the *Star* and C.K.S.O. companies.

Sudbury has already been assisted by grants from the Mason Estate. The Canadian Legion Memorial Hall, the Sudbury General Hospital, the Memorial Hospital, under construction, the Public Library, finished in 1952, the new Y.M.C.A.-Y.W.C.A. building, and many other projects have benefitted by Mason's posthumous generosity.

Despite the cosmopolitan nature of its population, comprising, it is claimed, twenty-six nationalities, Sudbury has a distinct individuality. Like people the world over, they have different personal characteristics, yet Sudburians in the mass have characteristics in common that distinguish them from any other community. The principal factor that makes Sudbury people so much alike, in spite of varying origins and early backgrounds is that nearly all of them come from somewhere else: they all have the pioneer spirit.

Even those from other parts of Canada feel when they decide to try their luck in Sudbury that they are undertaking a rare adventure, and although they find no Eskimos and few other evidences of subarctic existence, never quite lose their sense of identity with the pathfinders who have helped to open up the Canadian Shield.

While those who have come from continental Europe or the British Isles have much more reason to consider themselves pioneers, their feelings, too, are to a large extent based upon fantasy. Ukrainians, Finns, Poles, Italians and others have brought with them the antagonisms which caused them to migrate, and some derive great satisfaction in keeping these quarrels alive. But no plant can live without roots, and although valiant efforts have been made to transplant these precious plants to the soil of this new land, they do not become firmly rooted. For it is a fact that most of the younger generation, irrespective of their parents' origin or ideological beliefs, are much more interested in the fortunes of the Sudbury Wolves than in perpetuating the feuds of other lands.

Nevertheless, this tendency to standardization has its unfortunate side.   Undoubtedly these immigrant groups, with their fervour and capacity for loyalty to an idea, together with their music, songs, dancing and folklore can, and do, make a very desirable contribution to the cultural life of Canada, and it is to be regretted that these enriching strains tend sooner or later to die out.

When it comes to the greatness of Sudbury almost any Sudburian will debate the point with anyone.   Consequently when, after the 1951 census, the Bureau of Statistics announced that Sudbury had a population of 42,410 and that the city and surrounding district contained a total of 70,884, there was general disagreement.   By this time Sudbury had become accustomed to the claim that it had passed the 50,000 mark, and it was an affront to suggest that it was still so far short of that number.

There was less disagreement with the figure for the metropolitan area which, perhaps, is where the difference lay.   While it was natural that, with a rapidly growing and shifting population like that of Sudbury, census figures gathered in the summer of 1951 would be considerably exceeded by the time they were compiled for publication, they were probably not so far short of the true figure as Sudburians wished to believe.   The latter unconsciously count as Sudbury citizens many who actually live beyond its borders, for it must be remembered that the area actually within the city limits is relatively small.   On the other hand, no matter where these people may sleep, in every other sense they are citizens of Sudbury.

However, since other statistics are based upon them, the census figures will be used as a basis for the discussion of various aspects of Sudbury's population.   Figures for Sudbury city show the respective numbers of the principal national groups but, of course, not those in the metropolitan area.   Corresponding figures, however, are given for the Sudbury electoral district (as it was in 1951).

The largest group in the city consists of *Canadiens*, who number 16,060, with those from the British Isles next with

15,502. Since most of those belonging to the various European groups live in the Sudbury area, the district figures will prove fairly close for them. Thus while the city is shown to have 1,502 Italians, the district has 4,670, which is about the number claimed by Italians as correct for the city and surrounding area. Likewise, the 2,571 Ukrainians shown as living within the city, and 4,672 in the district, seems about right. Poles are shown as having 1,127 in the city and 2,006 in the district, which again is not far out. No figures are given for the Finns, one of the largest ethnic groups in the district, but Hannes Sula, editor of the Finnish newspaper *Vapaus*, who has been in the Sudbury district for thirty-five years, estimates that about 5,000 Finns live in the area, of whom 1,500 are in the city.

Although both Ukrainians and Finns are divided into bitterly antagonistic groups, determined to perpetuate their particular ideologies, they are making a definite contribution toward the life of Sudbury, the full impact of which will doubtless not become evident for many years to come. The qualities which sometimes estrange them from people of other backgrounds may be the very alloys needed to round out the blend that some day will be known as Canadian.

As Sudbury reached the sixtieth anniversary of its incorporation as a town, its people could look back on an interesting history and perhaps forward to an even more interesting one. It must be said, however, that for its size and importance Sudbury as a city is not imposing. Its streets are not laid out to the best advantage. It has few imposing business structures and the few that exist are often cheek by jowl with the most disreputable sort of shacks. The Cochrane-Dunlop building, mainly erected in 1894, still compares very favourably with the most recent.

Although The Wolves failed to capture the Allan Cup in the spring of 1953, after they had reached the semi-finals, Sudbury was proud to welcome curlers from all over Canada who gathered there in March, 1953, to play for the Macdonald Brier trophy in the annual bonspiel of the Dominion

Curling Association.   It was time, however, that Sudburians, while still worshipping at the shrine of sport, should
elevate their sights to take in activities at a slightly higher
cultural level, and with which most of them are still
unacquainted.

Now that the city has a suitable auditorium in the
Canadian Legion Memorial Hall, greater encouragement
could be given to concerts, plays, the ballet, etc.   The Little
Theatre Guild has been doing good work, but relatively few
are aware of its existence.   In 1947, under the leadership of
Rev. Father Thomas L. Mignault, the Sudbury Operatic
Society made a very creditable start.   In an interesting
booklet, *Sudbury a Musical City?*, the Society reviewed the
city's cultural resources, showing that it had already
produced many with more than usual talent and that only a
little encouragement was needed to produce others whose
talent might be of lasting value, not only to Sudbury, but to
all of Canada.   Unfortunately, when Father Mignault left
at the end of the year, the Sudbury Operatic Society ceased
to exist and most of the projects of promise that had begun
to thrive under its stimulus faded away.

Sudbury, a relatively wealthy community, can afford
anything it desires.   And while cultural activities cannot be
promoted in the same manner as popular sports, a tithe of
the money devoted to the latter judiciously spent in
encouragement of music, the drama, art appreciation, good
reading, and so forth, might in the end produce far greater
results.   It is perhaps significant that while there is only one
store in the city (Wolfe's) exclusively devoted to the sale of
books, there are two dozen outlets for beer.

# XXI

# *What of the Future?*

MINING IS A WASTING INDUSTRY AND THE inevitability of ending as a ghost-town is the skeleton in the closet of every mining community. This gives to many of them the temperaments of transients, perpetually haunted by a sense of insecurity. For this reason mining towns are deficient or even totally lacking in planning. No one cares to put money into buildings which, before their normal life-expectancy expires, may have to be abandoned. This has happened in more than one mining camp and will doubtless happen again. If no alternative industry can be developed in the meantime, a mining town must cease to exist after the mine or mines upon which it is dependent has ceased production. In most cases there is nothing else to do but move away.

How is the case with Sudbury? If its mines were to shut down tomorrow, Sudbury would be the biggest ghost-town in history, but of that there is fortunately little likelihood. In fact, as mining communities go, Sudbury, figuratively as well as actually, is built upon a rock. Nevertheless, while it can still look forward to a long life, the day must sometime come when the hoists will lift their last skip-loads of ore. That being the case, a wise community will not fold its arms and await the inevitable but consider what steps might be taken to avert disaster. Obviously the time to begin thinking about it is now, when the danger is remote and long-range planning can be

initiated.   The advantage of such planning is that details
can be modified from time to time in accordance with
changing conditions.

That Sudbury has become the world's nickel capital was
not due to the people of Sudbury.   The mines that have
made it what it is were developed by men coming from
outside, and with money that came from outside.   But it
is not likely that those who must plan for Sudbury's future
will also come from outside.   For that the people of
Sudbury themselves must be responsible.

Samuel Ritchie thought all would be well with the
nickel industry if he could but induce the navies of the
world to sheathe their ships in nickel-steel armour.   He
could not imagine the many uses for nickel that the Machine
Age would provide.   The jet-propelled airplane and the
expanding electronics industry, now in their infancy, were
beyond his power of imagination.   Stainless steel was still
shrouded in the shadows of the future.

Consequently, for us today to look fifty years ahead
would be ridiculous.   All we can be sure of is that anything
we might imagine will fall far short of the mark.   Is the
answer, then, to do nothing and Micawber-like wait for
something to turn up?   Fortunately, so far as Sudbury is
concerned, there is no need to do that.   Sudbury without
nickel-copper mines might be hard to imagine, but if,
beginning with alternatives that are obvious, advantage is
taken of opportunities as they occur, the transition from a
mining community to a busy industrial centre could be a
gradual process.

Such a programme could not be proposed for every town
that is so completely identified with mining as Sudbury,
but in its case the factors which may ultimately make this
possible are already in evidence: Possession of raw materials,
accessibility to markets, availability of technically trained
workers and potential power.

With nickel, copper, iron, cobalt and sulphur already
being produced in prodigious quantities, to which will
presently be added lead, zinc and further quantities of

sulphur from mines in the interior of the Basin, it may be assumed that the supply of raw materials will not fail. To the above might be added kyanite, extensive deposits of which have been discovered a few miles east of the city. It has a great many uses, but is used more especially in the manufacture of fire brick. The place of uranium in the world's economy, both as a source of power and as raw material, is still so vague as to be even too speculative for discussion in such a chapter as this. But it can be added as another of Sudbury's assets that immense quantities of uranium-bearing ore have been found within a relatively short distance.

The St. Lawrence-Great Lakes Waterway will provide a highway to the markets of the world. It would be better, of course, if Sudbury were actually situated on the Great Lakes, but considering the fact that it is already an established city, possessing facilities which years are required to provide, the thirty-odd miles between it and the lakeshore is not a fatal handicap.

Lack of power is one of the reasons why Sudbury is not already an important manufacturing centre. Again ignoring the implications of uranium, which would put every place largely upon terms of equality with every other, Sudbury's best hope lies in gas or oil from the Great Plains of western Canada. As the search for oil and gas continues into the North, Sudbury is more likely to find the oil and gas companies knocking at its door. As competition for markets becomes keener, pipe lines to the East will multiply. Furthermore, as oil and gas development extends northward the possibility of Sudbury's being within reach of a pipe line increases proportionately. A pipe line to Montreal by a great circle route would bring it considerably farther north than Sudbury, but not too far for a spur line.

The fact that oil and gas would be accessible along a zone so far north would doubtless, in time, result in the development of minerals and other resources in areas thus opened up. Sudbury could, of course, count on its share of this new-found business.

Then, of course, the possibility of much nearer development resulting from the discovery of oil or gas in the
palaeozoic rocks of the Hudson Bay Lowland, bordering the
west shore of James and Hudson bays, must not be ruled
out.   On theory, the rocks in that region should produce
oil, but covered as the country is by a thick mantle of post-
glacial drift overlain by muskeg, it is not easy to determine
the nature of the underlying formations.   Such little
prospecting as has already been done suggests that the
strata lie too flat to admit of oil concentration, but over
large sections practically no prospecting has yet been done.
As in other places, the drill must be the final arbiter.

Mining calls for a greater or less degree of technical
training, and Sudbury already has a population containing
a high percentage of technical knowledge, but it employs
chiefly men, and this leaves large numbers of women with
little or no opportunity to earn an independent living.
Even if there were no other reason, it should be imperative
that some industries at least should be established to take
advantage, in the interest of the national economy, of this
unemployed labour force which, as time goes on, will
increase rather than decrease.

So, assuming that the way out for Sudbury is to become
a manufacturing centre, the sooner a start is made the
better.   Let us see, then, what kinds of industry are already
represented.   Most of the industries at present in the city
are more in the nature of wholesale or other supply agencies
than they are manufacturing concerns.   The Canada Creo-
soting Co. Ltd., on Copper Cliff Road, which treats poles
and other wood products with creosote, is an exception and
there are a number of woodworking and metalworking
shops, but none that can rightly be listed as factories.

According to a comparative survey made in 1951[1],
Sudbury had about twenty-five industries of the type
referred to above, while Kitchener, with slightly less

[1]Baine, R. P.: *The Settlement of Sudbury Region*, a thesis presented for
M.A. degree in the University of Toronto, 1952.

population, had approximately 150. Kitchener occupies the centre of a prosperous agricultural region and at present is much closer to its markets than Sudbury would be, and has cheaper power, but the contrast need not be so great. If the matter were properly studied, as it soon must be, there is little doubt that opportunities for the establishment of light manufacturing could readily be found.

If this is not done, Sudbury will experience a growing migration of such young men as cannot fit into the mining picture and a large part of its young women. The mining companies are interested in promoting greater immigration in order to secure a constant supply of mine workers, but the supply will always run short of their needs unless the community provides an opportunity for more than one member of a family to find a job.

Providing assorted light manufacturing in order to make jobs for excess labour already on the spot is only a short-range phase of a long-range programme. The latter will undoubtedly be concerned with heavy industry. This in turn is predicated upon the progressive development of the Canadian Shield along with the rest of Canada, resulting in the establishment of new communities in northern Ontario, on the prairies, in Peace River and in the Mackenzie Valley, all of which might be considered tributary to a manufacturing centre at Sudbury.

This is not so visionary as it may seem. The three factors that will chiefly contribute toward a rapid growth for Canada in the years immediately ahead are very real. They are: oil in the West, minerals in the Canadian Shield and completion of the St. Lawrence-Great Lakes Waterway. Development of the first two is already under way and nothing short of another depression can stop it. And now that Canada has taken the decision to build the waterway alone if necessary, it is only a matter of time till it becomes a reality.

One activity gives rise to many others. The iron ore of Labrador is a case in point. In order to get it to the United States market, the Waterway becomes essential and interests, in a position to put pressure to bear where it counts most, and who might otherwise have been disinterested or opposed, now become its ardent advocates.

The hundreds of millions of dollars being invested in searching and drilling for oil cannot fail to produce their quotas of both. The producers of this oil and gas must find markets for it; at present the largest markets are in the East, and pipe lines to the East will follow as a matter of course. Oil and gas will add to existing power resources in the East, and this will lead to the establishment of additional industries. The mines will not only supply raw material for these new industries, but also markets for their products.

It is inconceivable that the domestic market will increase as fast as the volume of new factory products, a large part of which must find markets elsewhere. Here the St. Lawrence-Great Lakes Waterway again enters the picture, bringing the cheapest form of transportation to the doors of Canadian factories in an area extending inland over two thousand miles from the sea.

All this, of course, is assuming that everything goes according to schedule, but almost nothing ever does. The industrial programme outlined here, for Canada and for Sudbury, may take a generation or two to work out, and events as they occur will likely be different from what can be envisaged from today's vantage point. Yet in order to plan the initial steps it is necessary to have at least a tentative idea of the prospective goal, no matter how far in the future it may be.

When Sudbury began in 1883, no one then, nor for many years afterwards, had the merest inkling of what it was destined to become. But at that time the future of Canada itself was largely hidden from view. During the intervening years, Canada has followed a course which seems to have been inevitable; and in the light of that experience, it may be possible to predict in a general way its course for at least a few years ahead. Canada's course is determined

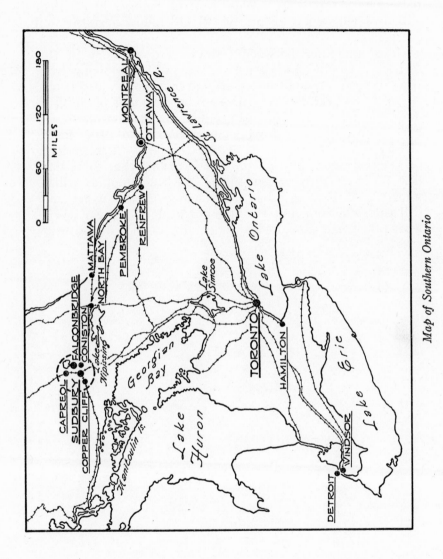

Map of Southern Ontario

to a certain extent by events, but the manner in which it will deal with such events will likely follow a traditional pattern.

The difference between Canada and Sudbury in this respect is that Canada's way of life, while changing from time to time, need not necessarily ever come to a dead stop. There is no doubt that a measure of national planning is desirable, but there is no need to plan for an eventual switch from its established course. Sudbury, on the other hand, although the letters may be ever so tiny, can see the writing on the wall, and that legend gives warning that some day, perhaps in the dim, distant future, the last ton of ore will be mined. Sudburians have no present cause for worry, nor will their children, but the thoughtful among them will at least take some thought for the coming of that distant day.

# INDEX

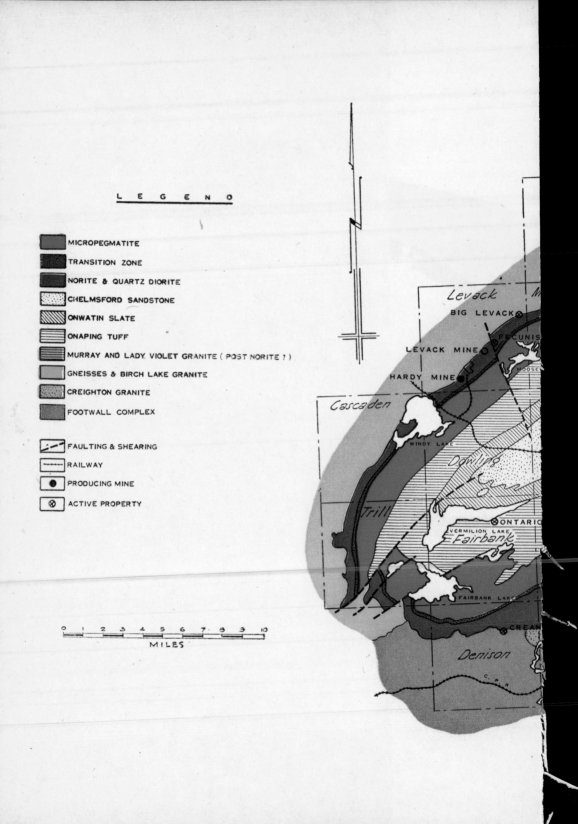

L E G E N D

MICROPEGMATITE

TRANSITION ZONE

NORITE & QUARTZ DIORITE

CHELMSFORD SANDSTONE

ONWATIN SLATE

ONAPING TUFF

MURRAY AND LADY VIOLET GRANITE ( POST NORITE ? )

GNEISSES & BIRCH LAKE GRANITE

CREIGHTON GRANITE

FOOTWALL COMPLEX

FAULTING & SHEARING

RAILWAY

PRODUCING MINE

ACTIVE PROPERTY

0  1  2  3  4  5  6  7  8  9  10
MILES

Levack          M

BIG LEVACK

FECUNIS

LEVACK MINE

MOOSE

HARDY MINE

Cascaden

WINDY LAKE

Dowling

Trill

ONTARIO

VERMILION LAKE

Fairbank

FAIRBANK LAKE

CREA

Denison

C.P.R.